OUR DEVELOPING WORLD

UNIVERSITY OF PITTSBURGH AT BRADFORD

LIBRARY

OUR DEVELOPING WORLD

by

L. DUDLEY STAMP

FABER AND FABER
24 Russell Square
London

*First published in mcmlx
by Faber and Faber Limited
24 Russell Square London W.C.1
First published in this edition mcmlxiii
Reprinted mcmlxv
Printed in Great Britain by
Latimer Trend & Co Ltd Plymouth
All rights reserved*

© *L. Dudley Stamp
1960*

*For copyright reasons this book may not
be issued on loan or otherwise except in its
original soft cover*

CONTENTS

Author's Note to the 1963 Edition	page 9
Preface	11
I. The Problem	13
II. The World's Population	17
III. The World's Lands	37
IV. Food for All	65
V. The New Agricultural Revolution	80
VI. The Pedological Paradox	90
VII. The Measurement of Land Resources and Farming Efficiency	103
VIII. The Balance of Power	123
IX. Minerals	138
X. Status Quo—Land and People	151
XI. Poor Little Rich Girl	162
XII. Poor Relations—The Under-Developed Countries	174
XIII. Quo Vadis?	180
Index	189

ILLUSTRATIONS

1. Population changes 1953–56	*page* 16
2. Population density by political units *c.* 1956	22
3. Population density, generalized distribution	23
4. Age-composition, Great Britain 1891	28
5. Age-composition, Great Britain 1947	28
6. Age-composition, Great Britain 1957	28
7. Age-composition, United States 1947	28
8. Age-composition, United States 1957	28
9. Age-composition, Australia 1956	29
10. Age-composition, Canada 1957	29
11. Age-composition, Israel 1956	29
12. Age-composition, India 1931	29
13. Age-composition, Ceylon 1955	30
14. Age-composition, Japan 1956	30
15. Age-composition, France 1956	30
16. Possible emigration effect, Great Britain	30
17. Age-composition of population of selected countries	32
18. World Regions classified by types of demographic situation (United Nations)	34
19. The cold lands of the Northern Hemisphere	41
20. Mountainous areas of the World	43
21. Arid areas of the World	43
22. Total negative areas	45
23. Climatic regions after Herbertson	48
24. Climatic regions after Finch and Trewartha	49
25. Wheat yields in Britain and the United States	67
26. Corn (maize) yields in the United States	67
27. Wheat yields and rainfall in South Australia	67
28. Agriculture in Europe, intensity (Huntington and Van Valkenburg)	106

ILLUSTRATIONS

29. Agriculture in Europe, variability (Huntington and Van Valkenburg) *page* 107
30. Graph of World Production of Coal 131
31. Graph of World Production of Oil 131
32. The World's Oil Producers 134
33. The Principal Sources of Petroleum 135
34. Graph of World Production of Zinc 142
35. Graph of Gold Production in Australia 142
36. Chief Sources of Bauxite 147
37. Chief Sources of Copper 147
38. Chief Sources of Tin Ore 147
39. Graph of World Production of Cocoa 173
40. The Developed and less Developed Countries of the World (FAO) 177
41. National Incomes of the World (in part after D. W. Fryer) 178
42. Population and Improved Land in England and Wales 183

(*Figs.* 30, 31, 32, 34, 35 *and* 39 *reproduced by permission of Longmans Green & Co. Ltd.*)

AUTHOR'S NOTE TO THE 1963 EDITION

This book was first published in 1960 and was reprinted with some minor corrections and additions in 1961, a few months later.

Since that time the results of censuses in a number of important countries—U.S.A. (1960), U.S.S.R. (1959), India and Pakistan (1961) and the United Kingdom (1961) as well as many others have become available. There is little doubt that the world's population now exceeds 3,100,000,000 and the annual net increase has advanced to at least 1·8 per cent. The problems discussed in this book are becoming daily more acute. I have taken the opportunity therefore of bringing up to date some of the population figures and tables.

As I pointed out in the note to the second printing, I am concerned primarily with the pressure of population on land and its physical resources and I have tried to give the facts objectively. It is not part of my purpose to suggest solutions to the problems raised; I have not considered the parts which capital and politics may play. The contrasts between nations will be obvious and it becomes clear that the world could continue to feed itself were it not for the man-made barriers which divide the nations.

L.D.S.

AUTHOR'S NOTE TO THE 1963 EDITION

PREFACE

In the spring of 1950 it was my privilege to be invited by the University of Indiana to deliver the Patten Foundation Lectures for that year. Under the bequest of Mr. Will Patten of Indianapolis, who graduated A.B. at Indiana University in 1893, there is to be chosen annually a Visiting Professor who resides on the Campus and has every opportunity of meeting for informal exchange of views those of the resident staff and students who may be interested in his field of work. I chose as my topic the Underdeveloped Lands. The six lectures were afterwards expanded and published jointly by the Indiana University Press and the American Geographical Society under the title of *Land for Tomorrow* early in 1952. In the summer of 1952 I revised some paragraphs and brought some tables up to date for the English edition published in 1953 as *Our Undeveloped World*. The American edition was subsequently reprinted without alterations.

It is symptomatic of the rapidity of world change that lectures prepared less than ten years ago and a book published only six years ago should read almost as historical documents. When I came to think of preparing a new edition it was clear that nothing less than a complete rewrite, indeed a new book, was necessary. Although I have incorporated where appropriate much material from the former books, this present volume is entirely new. Although my viewpoint remains fundamentally the same, many of the facts on which earlier conclusions were based have become much more precisely known, many new developments have taken place, and new thinking is needed. It is a process of rapid evolution rather than revolution and certainly little in the world of today can be described as static.

I can only hope that, in attempting to clarify my own ideas by setting them down on paper, I may induce others to join with me in looking beyond the problems of the moment, however important, to some aspects of the fundamental problem which to my mind lies behind them all in our fast developing world.

April 1960

L. D. S.

I

THE PROBLEM

The fundamental problem which faces the world today is the rapidly increasing pressure of population on physical resources, particularly on resources of land.

On the one hand the area of the earth's land surface is fixed and, broadly speaking, inextensible. Regarded as a national effort the Dutch reclamation of the former Zuyder Zee is adding considerably to the land area of the Netherlands, but in terms of world land area it increases the whole by only an infinitesimal fraction. There are no new lands to be discovered, the last remaining tracts are now being accurately delineated on maps and even since the predecessor of this book was published in 1953 we have learnt with considerable accuracy the extent of the last remaining unexplored land—the continent of Antarctica.

On the other hand the world's population continues to expand and, what is even more significant, is expanding more rapidly than ever before in the earth's history. On the whole birth rates are tending to decline but the net rate of increase is higher than ever for the simple reason that the knowledge and practice of death control have been expanding more rapidly than the knowledge and practice of birth control. The advance of medical techniques, combined with the spread of health services, has rendered many formerly killing diseases of minor importance with consequent far-reaching effects on maternal and infant mortality, expectation of life and longevity. There are now few remaining parts of the world where a modern-style census has not yet been taken: every year we know with greater accuracy both total population and rate of increase.

Against the background of a fixed land area of 57,168,000 square miles—36,586,000,000 acres or 14,812,000,000 hectares—we see a world population estimated on 1st July 1962 at 3,100,000,000. I give later in Chapter II the authority on which this estimated total rests and also for believing that the net rate of increase is over 1·8 per cent per annum or a net annual increase nearing 56,000,000. At this rate world population will double itself in less than 30 years—within the lifetime of many who will read these words. It may be only of theoretical interest to contemplate the approach towards standing room only—according to the statisticians of the United Nations, at the present rate there would only be a square metre each in 500 years time or by A.D. 2500, yet 500 years is such a short span of time compared with the 200,000 years since man's advent on the earth. Indeed as I write these words in my Cornish home I am watching the flames flicker cheerfully in a fireplace built more than 600 years ago. It is perhaps of more immediate and vital practical importance to wonder how we can accommodate and feed the 153,000 additional people who will be here on earth this time tomorrow.

The menace, real or supposed, of population pressure on land is nothing new. Under the extensive farming of the day it was probably a topic of conversation in the Middle Ages; it was certainly brought to the fore when Thomas Robert Malthus published the first edition of *An Essay on the Principle of Population as it affects the Future Improvement of Society* in 1798. Although in later editions the pamphlet was enlarged into a book and many of the highly original ideas expanded and modified, the fundamental thesis remained that population, if unchecked, increases in a geometric ratio, whilst sustenance increases only in arithmetical ratio: that population always increases up to the limits of the means of sustenance and is only checked by war, famine, pestilence and the influence of miseries derived from a consequent low standard of living. Following the fierce controversy aroused by his argument came a century of world expansion with development of new lands undreamed of by Malthus. But once more his arguments are very apposite —with the great differences that there are no new lands to be discovered, and few lands awaiting easy development, whilst the Malthusian checks of famine and pestilence are themselves held in check.

The immediate problem of population pressure on land can be studied on at least four levels. The first is the world or global level: we can say for example that each human being has a share of the earth's land surface of about 12 acres or 5 hectares. Reasons will be given later for suggesting that about 4 acres of this total can be regarded as potentially available for settlement and culvitation for food against a little over one acre at present so used. These are useful yardsticks but the world is far from being one united whole. How many people the land surface, with existing knowledge and techniques, could support is

THE PROBLEM

in fact of rather theoretical—I prefer not to insult our universities by saying academic—interest.

The second level of study is the national level, perhaps the most vital and significant. There are nations rich in land resources: some rich in total land area rather than in usable land, but others rich from any point of view. Such a one is the United States and it is inherently difficult for an American to appreciate the viewpoints of a nation whose whole way of life and thought is conditioned by shortage of land as it is in Japan. In Britain there is an overall shortage of land which makes it impossible for us as a nation to enjoy some of those advantages which are a commonplace in land-rich countries.

Most of the larger countries exhibit contrasts within their own boundaries. In some cases—one thinks of Brazil or Australia—the contrasts are extreme. Just as the solution to the problem may differ from one country to another, so it will then differ from one region to another, and we are in the realm of regional planning.

But there are also innumerable facets to the problem of local relationships between land and people. It is, or should be, the prime objective of town planning to secure for the people of the area the maximum advantages possible from an intelligent use of their land. They need space for living, but their livelihood depends upon the right location for industry and commerce; they need space for recreation, but if possible without sacrificing the land which can best produce fresh fruit, vegetables, milk and other foods; they need wide roads for easy access, but if possible without sacrificing the cultural heritage of the past enshrined in civil or ecclesiastical buildings. In the countryside too there is an intimate relationship between the farm and the farmer: although so many aspects of agricultural research are directed towards overcoming physical controls, it is abundantly clear that only certain types of land respond to or are suitable for the new techniques.

In the pages which follow each level of relationship between land and people will be studied. Although it is often argued that the effect of modern developments in transport and communications is to make the world smaller and to weld its constituent parts into a single whole, it is equally true that it brings into immediate contact regions sharply contrasted in almost every way, but especially in their levels of development. In a world where the declared aims of the democratic free countries include equal opportunities for all, the elimination of poverty and want and a more even distribution of wealth, it is unfortunately true that the immediate effect of closer contact is to heighten the contrasts

THE PROBLEM

between rich and poor, between the haves and the have-nots, between the overfed and the undernourished. It will be well to look first, therefore, at the overall world position and then to analyse some of these regional contrasts.

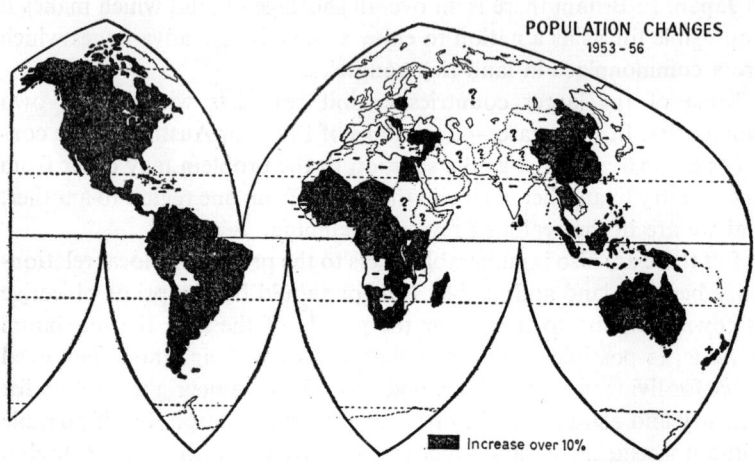

Fig. 1
The new lands of the Americas, Africa and Australia continue to show the most rapid population changes. (Data from United Nations)

II

THE WORLD'S POPULATION

The aspects of the work of the United Nations Organization which hit the newspaper headlines are the wrangles which go on in the Security Council or the General Assembly. All over the world the public remains little aware of the fine solid work achieved by U.N. agencies and departments of the permanent headquarters staff. In particular the Statistical Office is ceaselessly engaged in the collection and publication of a wide range of factual information. The Department of Social Affairs is concerned with data relative to population from all over the world and publishes the now indispensable *Demographic Yearbook* or *Annuaire Demographique*. In addition to standard tables with the latest available details of population country by country, a special subject is usually taken up in each annual volume. But besides the *Yearbook*, the Department publishes special reports, often of great general interest. One of the first of these was *World Population Trends, 1920-1947*, of which I made considerable use in *Our Undeveloped World*. It is an indication, however, of the serious attention which practically all countries are now giving to the population problem that the speculations I was forced to make when writing in 1950 when attempting to reach a figure for total world population as well as for its rate of growth are now mainly of historical interest. Few countries now remain where a census on modern lines has not yet been taken. For a large part of the world a decennial census is now the rule. When this book was being written in 1960, the last census year was 1950 (United States) or 1951 (United Kingdom, India, Pakistan and many Commonwealth countries) but many countries publish official estimates annually. In the United States a daily running total is kept and attracts great public interest. For long a major element of uncertainty was always present in the varied estimates for China: in 1953 a first census on modern lines gave a firm figure more than 25 per cent higher than previous estimates. After a long period of silence the U.S.S.R. published figures relative to 1956, based on careful estimates, though a full census was planned for 1959 and has

THE WORLD'S POPULATION

duly been carried out. Census returns for the United States in 1960, the British Isles in 1961 and for many other countries in 1960 and 1961 have now become available and have been used in revising many details which follow.

TABLE I

SUMMARY OF WORLD POPULATION FROM STATISTICAL OFFICE OF THE UNITED NATIONS

Continent and Region	1920	1930	1940	1950	1960	Possible error per cent	Area[1] sq. km. (thousands)	Density per sq. km. 1960
World Total	1,810	2,013	2,246	2,476	2,995	5	135,089	22
Africa	140	155	172	199	254	5	30,132	8
Northern	46	51	57	70	88	5	10,168	9
Tropical and Southern	94	104	115	129	166	5	19,964	8
America	208	244	277	330	405	1	41,985	10
North	117	135	146	168	199	0·5	21,483	9
Central	30	34	41	51	66	2	2,745	24
South	61	75	90	111	140	2	17,757	8
Asia (excluding U.S.S.R.)	967	1,073	1,213	1,360	1,679	5	27,082	62
South-West	44	48	54	64	77	5	5,589	14
South-Central	326	362	410	465	559	1	5,144	109
South-East	110	128	155	168	214	5	4,488	48
East	487	535	594	663	829	10	11,861	71
Europe (excluding U.S.S.R.)	328	355	380	393	427	0·5	4,929	86
Northern and Western	115	122	128	133	142	0·5	2,252	63
Central	112	120	127	128	139	0·5	1,014	137
Southern	101	113	125	132	146	1	1,663	86
Oceania	8·8	10·4	11·3	13·0	16·5	1	8,558	2
U.S.S.R.	158	176	192	181	214	1	22,403	10

[1] Area includes land area and inland waters, but excludes uninhabited polar regions and some uninhabited islands. Consequently density is proportionately higher.

THE WORLD'S POPULATION

The annexed table gives the estimates of world population published by United Nations for each ten years from 1920 to 1960. For mid-1960 it gives a total of 2,995,000,000. Allowing an error of 5 per cent either way the lower and upper limits are between 2,845,250,000 and 3,144,750,000. Applying the annual rate of increase discussed in the next section the world population at mid-1962 may be postulated as lying between 2,948,000,000 and 3,258,000,000 with 3,103,000,000 as a middle figure. In round figures there are probably over 3,100,000,000 people in the world in the year of grace 1962.

World Population Increase

However staggering the figures for total world population may be, it is the present rapid net increase which has turned attention almost everywhere to the need for a stocktaking of resources, especially of land and its capacity for the production of food, raw materials and supplies of energy.

In the past, even the recent past, the rate of increase, evidenced usually by such readily visible signs as large numbers of young children, only called attention to itself in certain parts of the world. It became difficult to refer to China without mention of China's teeming millions —for some reason millions did not seem to teem elsewhere—or to the 'yellow peril' which took in the population expansion of both China and Japan. Other areas were India, with the seemingly hopeless poverty of its masses; in Europe one thought almost instinctively of the innumerable *bambinos* of Italy. These old ideas, in part misconceptions, die hard, but the world pattern of today is very different.

To some extent the modern increasingly accurate estimates of population invalidate earlier attempts to calculate world population. Thus, writing in the late nineteen-thirties, the late Dr. R. R. Kuczynski could do no more than say that the population of the world was between 1,880 and 2,260 millions. On the other hand the calculations made by Sir Alexander Carr-Saunders in *World Population*, published in 1936, for earlier periods remain valid, and are reproduced in the accompanying Table II, together with figures for 1950 from United Nations' sources. The table brings out two salient features. Working in 50-year periods rates of increase are as follows:

Period	Rate	Period	Rate
1650–1700	16·8 per cent	1800–1850	29·2 per cent
1700–1750		1850–1900	37·3 per cent
1750–1800	24·4 per cent	1900–1950	53·9 per cent

THE WORLD'S POPULATION

Thus in 300 years the annual rate of increase jumped from 0·3 to over 1·0, and in the past 50 years to over 1·8 at the present day.

The second lesson from the table is one of changing world distribution. Already crowded in 1650, the countries of Europe have held their relative position with roughly a quarter of mankind. Already overcrowded, Asia has declined relatively. The figures for Africa show all too plainly the long-continued effects of the slave trade added to internecine strife and primitive conditions. The New World of the Americas and Australia still have a long way to go before they are supporting the number of mankind proportionate to their areas.

TABLE II

POPULATION OF THE WORLD BY CONTINENTS, 1650–1960
(Millions)

Continent	1650	1750	1800	1850	1900	1950	1960
Europe	100	140	187	266	401	574[1]	641
North America	1	1·3	5·7	26	81	168	199
C. and S. America	12	11·1	18·9	33	63	162	206
Oceania	2	2	2	2	6	13	16
Africa	100	95	90	95	120	199	254
Asia	330	479	602	749	937	1,360	1,679
Total	545	728	906	1,171	1,608	2,476	2,995

Percentage Distribution

Europe	18·3	19·2	20·7	22·7	24·9	23·3	21·4
North America	0·2	0·1	0·7	2·3	5·1	6·8	6·6
C. and S. America	2·2	1·5	2·1	2·8	3·9	6·5	6·9
Oceania	0·4	0·3	0·2	0·2	0·4	0·5	0·6
Africa	18·3	13·1	9·9	8·1	7·4	8·0	8·4
Asia	60·6	65·8	66·4	63·9	58·3	54·9	56·1
	100·0	100·0	100·0	100·0	100·0	100·0	100·0

Before 1650 any 'estimates' of population are of the nature of guesswork. In the later days of the Roman Empire—about A.D. 400—200,000,000 has been suggested.

[1] Including U.S.S.R.

THE WORLD'S POPULATION

The Future Growth of World Population

In the words of the United Nations' publication with this title, 'it took 200,000 years for the world's human population to reach 2,500 million, it will now take a mere 30 years to add another 2,000 million. With the present rate of increase, it can be calculated that in 600 years the number of human beings on earth will be such that there will be only one square metre for each to live on. It goes without saying that this can never take place, something will happen to prevent it.'

The realization that the present rate of population increase is so alarming has come but very recently. The United Nations' Population Branch has made three attempts to calculate the growth of population up to 1980. The first estimates were prepared in 1951 and gave a total for 1980 between 2,976 and 3,636 million—the difference between the figures being 660 million.[1] In 1954 revised estimates gave a total in 1980 between 3,295 and 3,990 million.[2] Then in 1958 on the basis of improved information and more detailed methods an estimate was published for 1980 of between 3,850 and 4,280 million, a range of 430 million.[3]

These successive estimates, made over a short span of eight years, illustrate three points. First, the rapid improvement of factual knowledge, notably the new figures for China. Second, that improved knowledge has resulted in an upward adjustment of the estimates. Third, that the margin of error is decreasing and we may certainly look forward to a world population of well over 4,000,000,000 by 1980, and to between 7,000 and 8,000 millions by the end of the century. Yet even as late as in a paper published in January 1950 Julian Huxley was bold in asserting the world population might reach 3,000 million by A.D. 2000. The United Nations' publication quoted considers that the evidence which has accumulated for the comparatively undisturbed conditions of the nineteen-fifties suggests that (a) current and future declines in mortality are likely to be substantial; (b) birth-rates in countries of high fertility are not very likely to decrease very soon; and (c) in most countries of comparatively low birth-rates, renewed decreases in fertility do not appear imminent.

[1] The Past and Future Growth of World Population, *Population Bulletin of the United Nations*, 1st Dec. 1951.
[2] Framework for Future Population Estimates, 1950–1980, *Proc. World Population Conference*, 1954, 3, 283–328.
[3] The Future Growth of World Population, *United Nations Population Studies No. 28*, 1958.

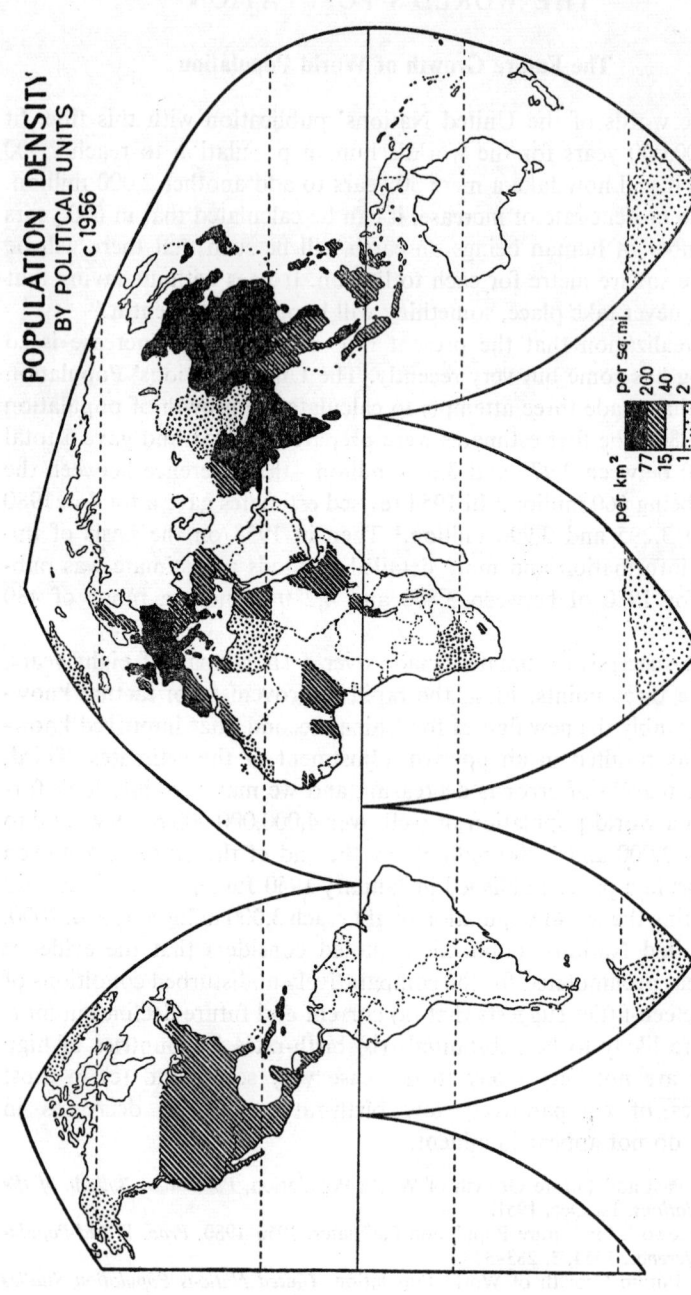

Fig. 2

The most populous countries are not generally the areas of most rapid population increase (see Fig. 1)

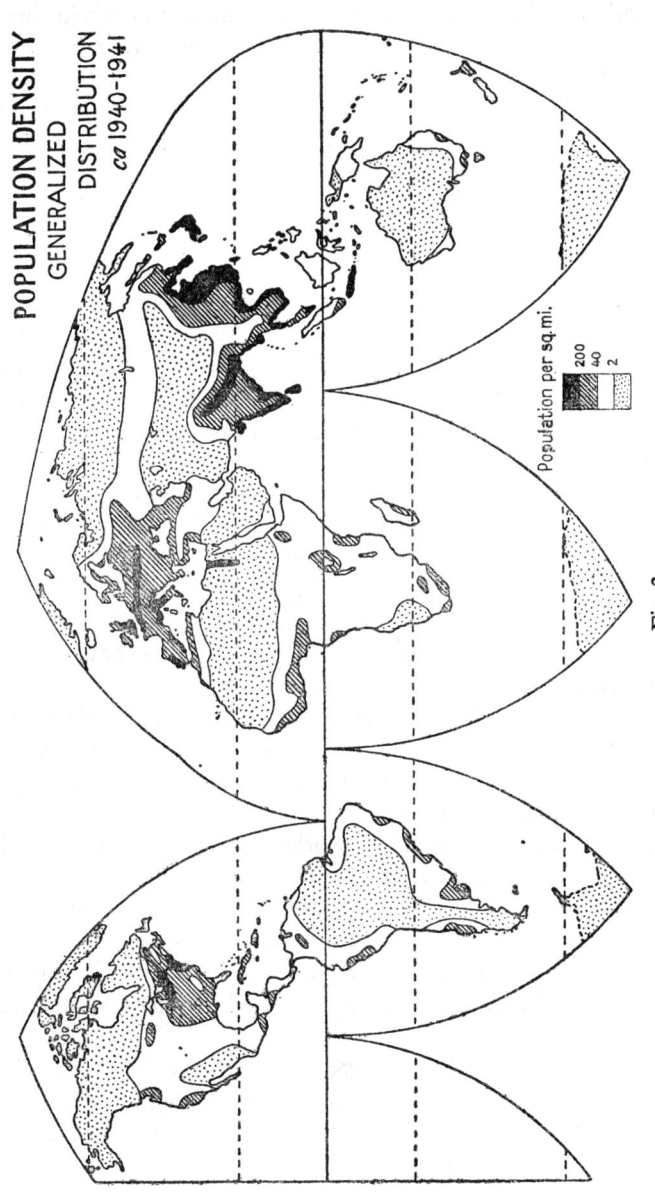

Fig. 3

A more accurate picture of the world's population is obtained by disregarding political units and plotting the actual distribution of people. The concentrations on the alluvial soils of Asia and in the industrialized areas of Europe and eastern North America are especially conspicuous

THE WORLD'S POPULATION

The spread of health services suggests that assumption (a) is justified, but the sharp, indeed spectacular, drop in the birth-rate in Japan indicates the possibility of similar changes elsewhere, especially in very thickly populated countries. On the other hand the rise in the birth-rate in the United States is a phenomenon of particular interest.

Death Control

Conscious as we are in the western world of the general practice of family limitation, it is difficult at first to believe that the net rate of population increase is more rapid than ever before. We remember naturally our Victorian grandparents and the numerous examples of families of ten or a dozen children, and we contrast that with the normal one- or two-children families of our contemporaries. We are apt to magnify, too, the toll of two world wars on human life until we look at the American, and to some extent our own, birth-rate in 1946 and especially 1947 in that mad rush to make up for lost years. What we do constantly forget is the sad wastage of human life in the past from diseases now entirely preventable. Queen Anne of England of revered memory (1665–1714) happily married and enjoying the best medical skill of the day, bore seventeen children only one of whom survived infancy, and he died at the age of eleven. Again and again on the tombstones of our country churchyards or the memorials on the walls we are reminded of the uncertainties of life to the young wife, noting that the tough ones who survived went on to the eighties or nineties.

In these days every country in the world has a story to tell of early survival and greater longevity. It is actually within the half-century since 1900 that the really spectacular discoveries in medicine have been made, with the result that the killing diseases even in the days of our own fathers are no longer feared. Every country in the world enjoys to a greater or less degree the benefits conferred by these recent discoveries.

In the first place maternal mortality at childbirth has been reduced in the more advanced countries almost to vanishing point. The average woman is likely to live the whole of her reproductive span of life whereas so many were formerly cut off in its midst.

THE WORLD'S POPULATION

TABLE III

CAUSES OF DEATH IN ENGLAND AND WALES PER 100,000 POPULATION

	1900	1956
Heart diseases	2,350	4,341
Cancer	829	2,112
Diseases of nervous system	1,271	1,792
Gastric and duodenal ulcers	47	120
Typhoid fever	173	nil
Diphtheria	292	nil
Scarlet fever	117	nil
Measles	391	1
Whooping cough	356	2
Pneumonia	1,374	519
Bronchitis	1,692	664
Tuberculosis	1,902	120
Childbirth		9
Accidents		489
Other causes		1,503
		11,672

In the second place there is an enormous reduction in infant mortality. The expectation of life for a child born alive has more than doubled in the past fifty years.

In the third place the old killing diseases which formerly attacked people of all ages have been very largely brought under control. This is true of the dreaded once-incurable tropical scourges such as malaria, yellow fever, plague, typhoid, cholera and leprosy as well as the diphtheria, pneumonia, tuberculosis, septic poisoning and venereal diseases of more temperate latitudes. Apart from the still unconquered cancers, the killing diseases of today are largely those of old age—natural failures of the heart and circulation or the respiratory system, of organs which have become worn out through long years of use or misuse consequent upon the new strains of modern life. But these diseases strike later and later: an ever-increasing proportion of the people survive into the sixties, the seventies, the eighties and beyond.

One obvious result of the present trend is the drop in the death rate—from old figures of 40 per thousand persons per year to 30, to 20 and less. Since the net increase is the excess of births over deaths, net increase is obviously greatest where birth-rate remains high, and there is little or no practice of birth control.

THE WORLD'S POPULATION

Social Factors in Population Increase

In countries where deliberate family planning is now usual, social factors exist which may play an unexpectedly large part. This is in fact a highly complex subject. It is well known that the cult for large families was, and in some countries still is, closely linked with a concept of security. For ageing parents there will be at least some of the children to look after us in our old age; in Victorian England it was the rule that at least one or more of the sons will carry on the family business. Potent factors in changing the latter concept have been inheritance taxes or death duties, whilst the high incidence of direct taxation, combined wtih increased standards of living, involve decisions among young married couples between a baby and a baby car or television. As the State has shouldered more and more the responsibilities for expenses of child-bearing, health, education and old age, and the Welfare State with its Womb to Tomb policies of social security has replaced individual initiative, there has been an encouragement to larger families among the lower income groups, but a reverse effect amongst the intelligentsia who refuse to bear children they cannot educate and bring up in the more individual ways they consider essential. There is thus the well-known phenomenon of families decreasing in size with a general increase in the standard of living. We may perhaps perceive in the United States the next stage, however, where, material wants satisfied, a larger family to share the material prosperity becomes both justified and desirable.

What may be called national anomalies certainly exist. Since the disaster of the Second World War and the closure of avenues of expansion, there has been a spectacular drop in the birth-rate in Japan. It is in part the result of legalized abortion, but it suggests a realization on a national scale that the country has attained the maximum population it can support, and that any hope of maintaining or increasing the standard of living depends upon a limitation of population.

The Changing Age Structure of the Population

The age structure of population is strikingly shown by what have come to be commonly called 'fir-tree' diagrams. Figs. 4 to 6 illustrate how markedly the position in Britain has changed over the past sixty or seventy years. The diagram for 1891 is typical of an expanding popu-

THE WORLD'S POPULATION

lation, as it was before the great medical advances of the present century, with the largest proportion of individuals, both male and female, in the lowest age group, 0–4 years inclusive. The second diagram, for 1947, shows the results of the increasing expectancy of life and the consequent greater number of old people, of the long-continued drop in the birth-rate, with a consequent bulge of population in the 35–39 age group. It also shows the remarkable jump in the birth-rate immediately after World War II, when so many young couples, separated or unable to live a normal life during the war, set to work to build up a family and make up for the lost years. The third diagram (Fig. 6) shows how, ten years later, the earlier 'bulge' had passed up on to the 45–49 age group, and how the post-war family building was now reflected in the school age groups 5–9 and 10–14 with the attendant problems for our educational authorities. The two later diagrams for Britain are illustrative of those countries of the Old World where voluntary limitation of families from whatever cause has already had a marked effect on the age composition of the population. The diagrams for the United States show clearly the effect of the great depression of the 'thirties, the incidence of the war years and the return to a virile prosperity after the end of the war. The same features appear in Australia (and other young expanding countries); in Canada the depression hit less severely than in the United States. Faith in a new life in a new land is strongly marked in Canada, still more so in Israel.

Turning to the diagrams for India in 1931 and Ceylon in 1955 we see the demographic characteristics of countries where medical skill is not yet sufficiently widespread to keep alive to a ripe old age the same proportion of the people as in other lands. The diagram for Japan is interesting because it shows the sudden recent change in the birth-rate.

The 1947 diagram for Britain suggests the disadvantages to the country of an emigration policy which would still further lower the numbers of younger wage-earners, but leave the same number of over-age dependants (Fig. 16). That whole sections of the population, including the elderly, should emigrate has been recognized by some receiving countries. For example, in recent years British migrants to Australia have been officially encouraged to take their parents with them, thus transferring whole families. It is still true, however, in the majority of immigrant countries that only the young and the young workers find a welcome, unless the older people can bring capital and are independent. Emigration from the overcrowded European countries may create as many problems as it solves. On the other hand,

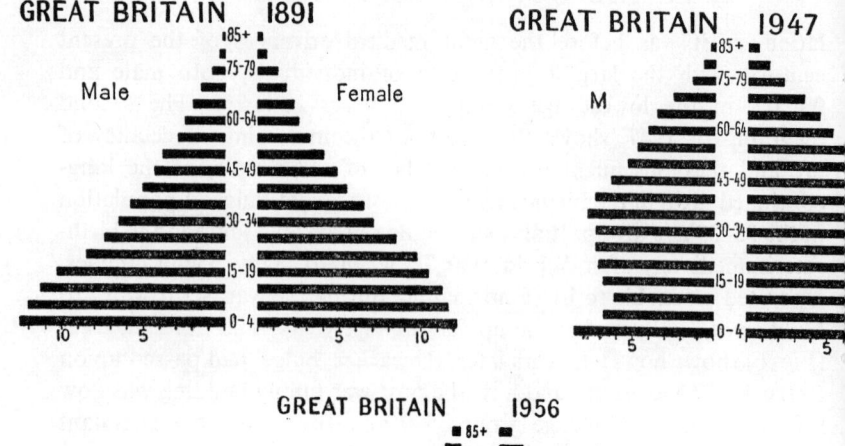

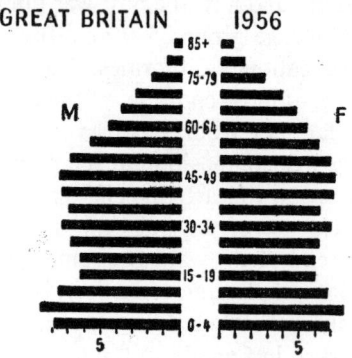

Figs. 4–6
Diagrams of age-composition of the population of Britain in 1891, 1947 and 1956

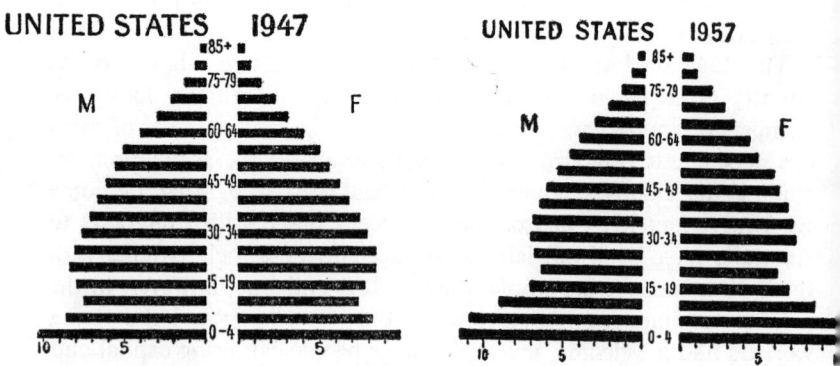

Figs. 7–8
Diagrams of age-composition, United States, 1947 and 1957

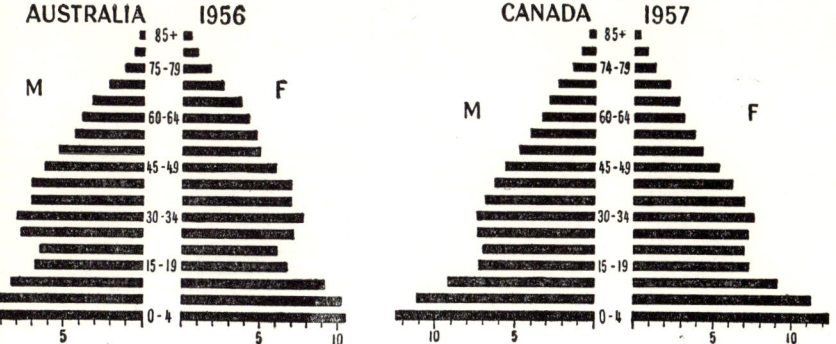

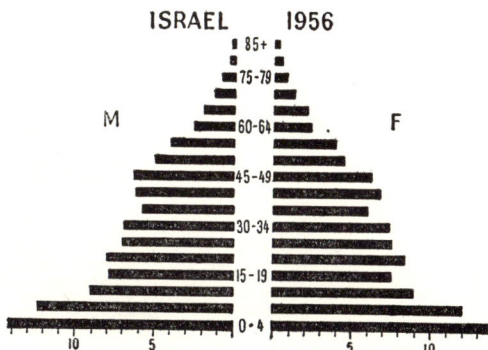

Figs. 9–11
Diagrams of age-composition in three 'new' lands

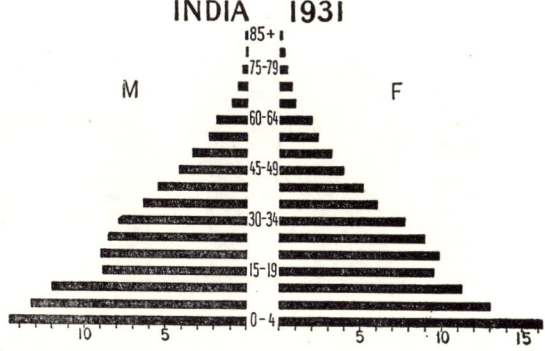

Fig. 12

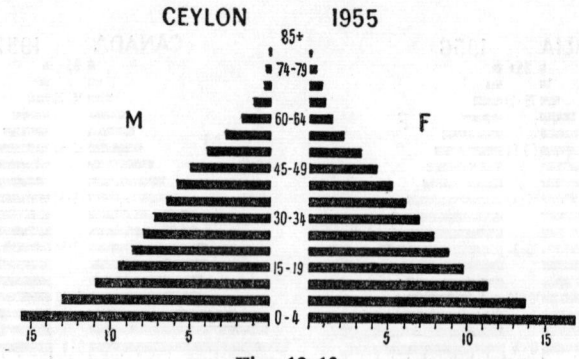

Figs. 12–13
Diagrams of age-composition in two 'old' Asiatic countries

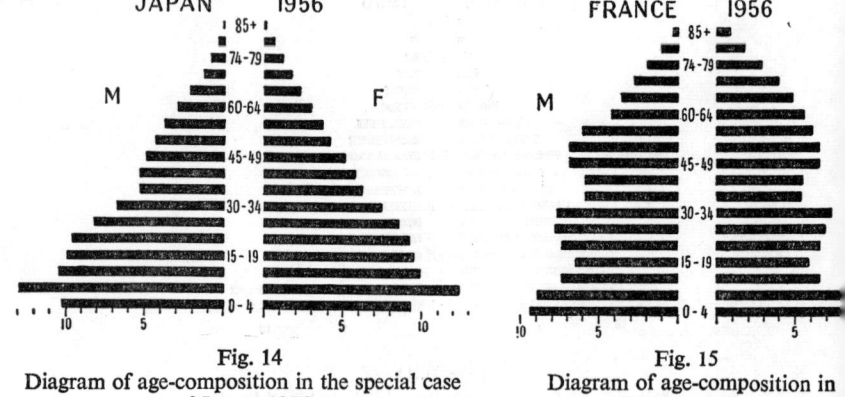

Fig. 14
Diagram of age-composition in the special case of Japan, 1956

Fig. 15
Diagram of age-composition in France, 1956

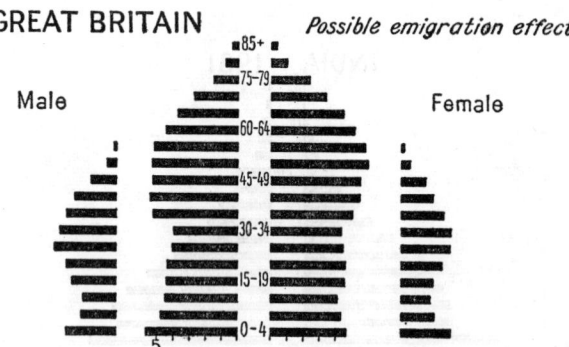

Fig. 16
Diagram showing possible effect of large-scale emigration on the British population. If the migration were of young people as shown by the detached parts, the population left behind would be hopelessly overbalanced by the aged

THE WORLD'S POPULATION

remittances from emigrant children to their parents in the homeland, such as dollar remittances from America to Greece and Italy, may play a large part in balancing trade.

In all countries problems of adjustment to a changing age structure are apparent. One, well seen in Britain, is the question of age of retirement. If pensionable age is 60, between 16 and 17 per cent—one person in 6—are now over that age. If retirement is deferred to 65 it is between 11 and 12 per cent—one person in 8 or 9. If retired persons are living on pension this is obviously an increasing burden on those in productive work, quite apart from the fact that men or women of the 60–70 age groups may be, in many respects, at the height of their powers. At the other end of the scale the raising of the school-leaving age as well as the increasing length of most forms of professional training mean that wage-earning and productive work are both postponed.

Some National Contrasts

In my previous book, *Our Undeveloped World*, I suggested that the countries of the world fell into four broad groups which could be readily distinguished by dividing their people into three main categories —the children and adolescents (0–19 years), persons of 'working' age (20–64) and over-age dependants (65 years and over).

In the first group (I) are the old countries of north-western Europe, such as Britain, Belgium, France, Denmark and the Netherlands, characterized by a very large proportion of old people, a large working population, and a relatively small number of young people.

In Group II I placed the countries of Asia and Africa, typified by India and Egypt, with very high birth-rates, but a low expectation of life, so that the numbers of young people are high, of old people low. In Group III, covering especially the Catholic countries of Latin America with plenty of land, there is a still higher proportion of children and young people. In Group IV, covering especially the 'new' countries of mid-latitudes, there are more young people than in the old crowded countries of Europe, whilst the proportion of old people is less.

These groups are illustrated in Fig. 17 reproduced from my earlier book and based on figures for 1940–47 (India 1931). I think my generalization remains in general true, (except for Japan), but in the accompanying table I have used 1955–57 figures.

THE WORLD'S POPULATION

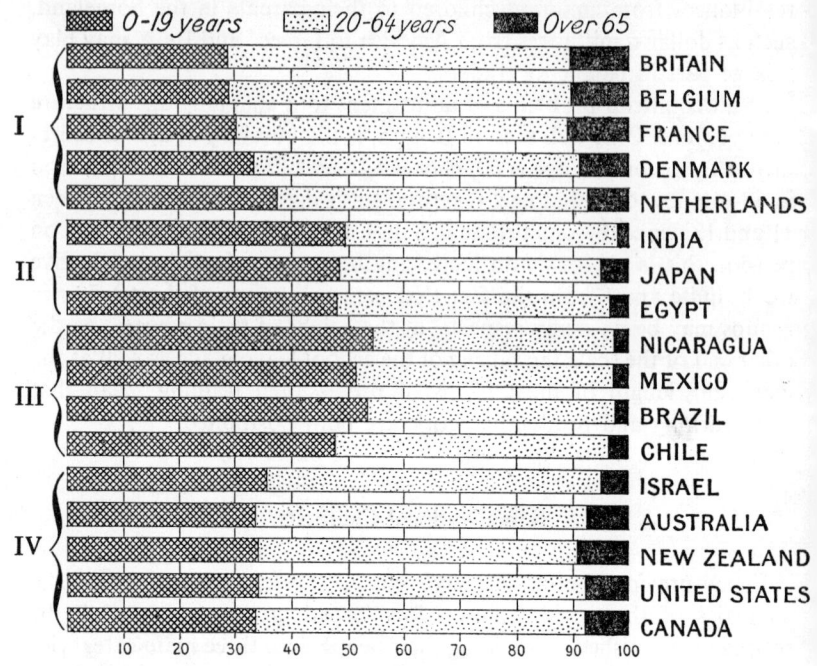

Fig. 17
Diagram summarizing the age-composition of the population of selected countries from four groups: I, the old settled countries of north-western Europe; II, countries of Asia and Africa; III, Latin American countries; IV, 'new countries' of mid-latitudes

In a recent publication of the United Nations, *The Future Growth of World Population*, 1958, the world was divided into nineteen regions and an instructive series of four maps shows these world regions classified by six 'types of demographic situation'. The four maps refer to 1930, 1950–55, 1975 according to 'high' and 1975 according to 'low' assumptions. The six types distinguished are:

1. High fertility, high mortality.
2. High fertility, mortality high but declining.
3. High fertility, moderate mortality.
4. Fairly high fertility, moderate mortality.
5. Moderate fertility, low mortality.
6. Low fertility, low mortality.

The accompanying map, Fig. 18, has been redrawn from this source. It will be seen that (1) and (2) are my Group II; (3) my Group III; (4) is only represented by Cuba and neighbouring West Indian islands in 1950–55; (5) is my Group IV and includes the U.S.S.R.; (6) is my Group I, to which Japan is now transferred.

TABLE IV

			Children and Adolescents 0–19 years	Normal Working Population 20–64 years	Over-age Dependants 65 and over
I	Britain	1956	29·0	59·5	11·5
	Belgium	1955	28·2	60·3	11·5
	France	1956	30·6	57·5	11·9
	Denmark	1956	33·6	56·4	10·0
	Netherlands	1955	37·5	54·1	8·4
II	Ceylon	1955	50·3	47·8	1·9
	India	1931	49·1	48·7	2·2
	Japan	1956	42·4	52·3	5·3
III	Peru	1956	58·4	42·2	3·0
	Brazil	1940	53·3	44·2	2·5
	Colombia	1951	52·8	44·1	3·1
IV	Canada	1957	40·1	52·3	7·6
	United States	1957	37·9	53·5	8·6
	Australia	1956	36·0	55·6	8·4
	New Zealand	1956	38·6	52·2	9·2
	Israel	1956	42·9	52·4	4·7

Are there Racial Contrasts?

The contrasts between one region of the world and another, between one nation and another, naturally lead one to ask if some of the contrasts are racial, if for this purpose one may use the dangerous word 'race' as merely signifying white or Indo-European, yellow and black. Any work along these lines is fraught with great difficulties and few such studies have been attempted. The German demographer Friedrich Burgdörfer (*Sterben die Weissen Volker?* 1934) attempted a brief survey of the position as between Europeans and non-Europeans. Carr-Saunders, in summarizing changes between 1650 and 1930, noted that the brown and yellow peoples had clearly made large actual gains with the likelihood that they had about maintained their proportion of world population. The black, or negro, peoples had suffered heavy relative losses. From having once formed about one-fifth the population of the world they now formed but one-fifteenth. It was the white peoples who gained most—from about 100,000,000 in 1650 to some 720,000,000

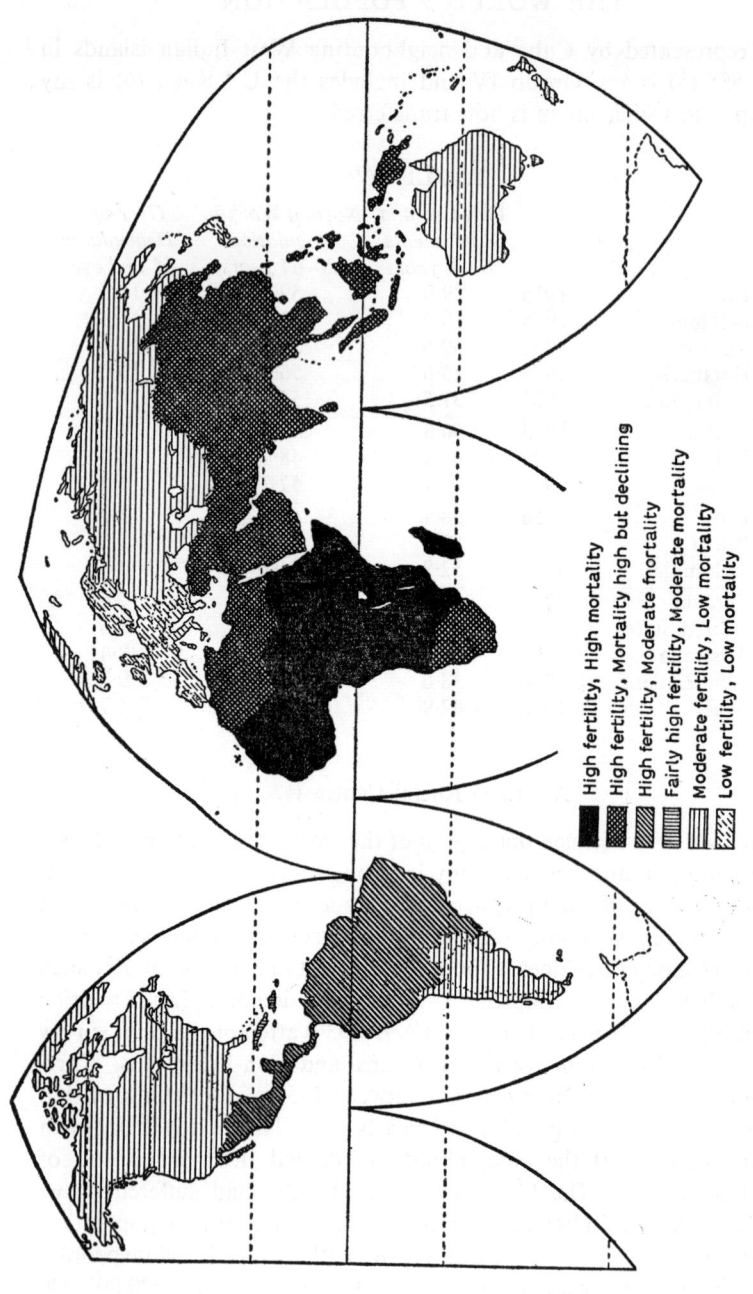

Fig. 18
World Regions classified by types of Demographic Situation, 1950–55 (Based on *The Future Growth of World Population*, United Nations Population Studies No. 28, 1958)

THE WORLD'S POPULATION

in 1930, or nearly double the rate of growth for the peoples of the world as a whole. We are perhaps more concerned with the position at the present day, and the trends for the future. Is it, for example, true that the white peoples now show a marked slowing down of population expansion, whereas it is now the turn of the negro population of Africa to show the most marked increases? There is a growing consciousness of the possibilities of the situation, and those who have followed certain negro literature will know of the discussion about the problems of 'absorbing the world's white minority'. The figures showing the growth of the 'white' continents, given above, clearly do not bear out this contention as yet, whatever the future may hold.

Taking, however, the present world population as 3,100,000,000 we can get a rough figure for the main racial divisions:

Yellow races (Chinese, Japanese, peoples of south-east Asia)		1,010 millions
Indo-European	White races	1,050 millions
	Brown races (Indian, peoples of south-west Asia and N. Africa)	760 millions
Black races		250 millions
Amerindians and mestizos		30 millions

Although it is not part of the scope of this book to deal with the languages of mankind, the position of English-speaking white peoples is of special interest. It was discussed by the late Professor C. B. Fawcett in 1947.[1] He estimated that they numbered 20·3 million in 1800–1 (15·9 million in the British Isles; 4·3 million in the United States) compared with 188 million in 1940–41 (119 million in the United States, 51 million in the British Isles; 9 million in Australia and New Zealand, 8 million in Canada). By 1963 we may say that the total had risen to about 249 million if we presume that recent immigrants into the United States, Canada and Australia are to be classed as 'English-speaking'. This total is made up of United Kingdom (53), Irish Republic (3), Canada (13), United States (165), South Africa (2), Australia (11) and New Zealand (2). Thus between 8 and 9 per cent of the world's peoples are English-speaking whites. They have increased nearly twelve-fold in the past century and a half, or four times as rapidly as the world's peoples as a whole. If one adds some 30–40 million coloured peoples whose mother-tongue is English, the English language easily

[1] The Number and Distribution of Mankind, *Scientific Monthly*, 64, 1947, 389–96.

THE WORLD'S POPULATION

leads as the first language of the greatest number of people, with one great exception—Chinese.

The Spatial Distribution of World Population

Seen from any point of view, the population of the world is very irregularly distributed. Spread evenly over the whole land surface the population at the time of writing would give an average density of 58 persons per square mile—about 12 acres per head or about 21 persons per square kilometre. The actual population density by political units is indicated approximately in Fig. 2 and generalized, ignoring political boundaries, in Fig. 3. Existing densities are related only in a general way to certain favourable climatic regions discussed in the next chapter, only in a very general way to other natural resources. These relationships we discuss in the chapters which follow.

III

THE WORLD'S LANDS

The surface of the earth, both land and water, is calculated to be 196,836,000 square miles—509,610,000 square kilometres, or 125,975,040,000 acres. Of this total between a quarter and a third or 57,168,000 square miles is land. In determining this total the greatest margin of error is with the area of Antarctica, since it is there possible that the land continent may be in two halves beneath the great ice cap. But in any case, should not the permanent ice be included in the 'land' area? With this reservation the continental areas using the figures given in hectares for total area, including inland water, by FAO are:

	Square miles	Hectares (million)	Acres (million)
Europe	1,903,000	493	1,218
U.S.S.R.	8,645,000	2,240	5,533
Asia	10,891,000	2,822	6,970
Africa	11,806,000	3,059	7,556
North and Central America	9,355,000	2,424	5,987
South America	6,855,000	1,776	4,387
Oceania	3,303,000	856	2,114
Antarctica	4,410,000	1,142	2,821
	57,168,000	14,812	36,586

Taking the largest political units, the British Commonwealth ranks first in area with about 10 million square miles (1962), the Union of Socialist Soviet Republics is second with 8⅔ million, followed by the United States with 3¾ million, Brazil with 3¼ million and China with 3 million.

Neither these figures nor those of the areas of the continents have

THE WORLD'S LANDS

much practical meaning. We are concerned primarily with those parts of the earth's surface which are permanently settled by human beings, or which have the physical conditions which render them capable of being permanently settled and developed.

The Habitable Globe

Man will always be lured by special circumstances, notably the occurrence of economic minerals, to invade and settle at least temporarily the most inhospitable parts of the earth's surface. But where settlement is linked with the cultivation of the land, the use of pastures or the exploitation of forests, it is limited by various physical factors. Geographers are accustomed to refer to 'negative areas'—that is areas which are broadly uninhabited and in most cases likely to remain so. What are the chief factors responsible for this negative character?

In the first place we may eliminate the areas permanently covered by ice and snow. Apart from Antarctica there is the great Greenland icecap, covering such a large proportion of that lofty island that only small tracts around the fringes are ice-free. There are also huge areas where the snow cover may disappear for a short period, but which are beyond the possibility of normal human settlement This is the case over a large part of northern Canada and the associated Arctic islands. We have only recently begun to study and understand the permafrost zone—that is, those areas where the heat of summer is insufficient to do more than just thaw the surface layers, and where the soil or subsoil is permanently frozen at depth. The permafrost areas in Canada, Alaska and the U.S.S.R. are estimated to cover some 5 million square miles which, with Antarctica and Greenland, comprise one-fifth of the world's land surface. Even outside the permafrost zone there are huge areas where the summer growing season is too short for crop cultivation, though sparse settlement dependent upon pastoral occupation or fishing may be possible.

Then we can eliminate large areas of the earth's surface which are occupied by mountains and plateaus where the land is either too rugged or too lofty to permit settlement depending on cultivation. In total more than another fifth of the earth's surface falls into this category. There are large areas where precipitation is insufficient to support more than the scantiest of vegetation—the deserts or arid regions. In general they are the lands where precipitation in terms of rainfall is less than

10 inches a year in mid or high latitudes, less than 20 inches in the tropics. Where water is available from underground sources or from rivers arising in adjacent humid lands, irrigation is possible and cultivation and settlement may result; but over huge areas there is no such possibility, and almost certainly another fifth of the earth's surface can be eliminated on grounds of aridity, at least with methods of watering now at our command. Except in the rarest cases, the occurrence of minerals of economic importance is not conditioned by climate, and mining settlements may be, and are, found in areas where settlement would otherwise be ruled out.

If we regard the habitable lands as those having physical and climatic conditions permitting the growth of crops desired by man, the area available does not cover more than two-fifths of the land surface. Even then, much more must be eliminated because of the absence or poverty of soil or because of excessive rainfall.

Including Antarctica, a present-day world population of 3,100,000,000 means an allotment of about 12 acres a head, or an average density of 58 persons per square mile (about 21 per square kilometre). If Antarctica is excluded these figures are changed to 10·9 acres a head and an average density of 59 per square mile (22 per square kilometre).

Habitable and Inhabited Areas

The optimists are fond of pointing to the fact that there are huge areas of the earth's surface, apparently well watered, supporting a luxuriant or at least an adequate natural vegetation, but which at the present day are either sparsely populated or almost uninhabited. The outstanding example is, of course, the great Amazon basin of South America—some 2 million square miles. If for a moment we regard these tracts as 'habitable' we see that there is a marked contrast between the habitable and the actually inhabited areas of the earth.

A number of years ago the late Professor C. B. Fawcett[1] came to the conclusion that the extent of the cultivable land of the earth was 30 per cent of the total land area, that is about 17 million square miles. In so far as permanent settlement depends on cultivation, this is equivalent to saying habitable area. He noted that another 30 per cent might be classed as productive but not cultivable—forest and poor grazing land, with mountain and hill pastures, semi-arid ranch and bush—but the

[1] 'The Extent of the Cultivable Land', *Geographical Journal*, LXXVI (1930), 504–9.

THE WORLD'S LANDS

remainder (40 per cent) he estimated as occupied by the deserts, dry and cold. The wet forested lands of the hot belt he included in the cultivable lands as the regions offering the chief possibilities for extension of cultivation.

We get the same figure by taking, as we have just done, a fifth of the earth's surface as too cold, a fifth too mountainous and a fifth too arid for settlement, and adding 10 per cent where little or no soil exists over naked rock.

The figure of 30 per cent of the land surface cultivable would give us 11,000 million acres—rather less than 4 acres per head of population. What area is actually cultivated at present?

World Land Use

The Food and Agriculture Organization of United Nations now collects officially details of land use. As more, or more accurate, information becomes available, the estimates are revised. At the time of writing the estimates published in the *Yearbook* for 1957 and relating in general to 1955–56 give the following details.

TABLE V

WORLD LAND USE, 1955–56

Million hectares

	Total area	Arable or cropped	Permanent meadows and pastures	Forested land	Other land
Europe	493	151	85	138	119
U.S.S.R.	2,240	220	267	742	1,011
Asia	2,822	426	434	514	1,448
Africa	3,059	232	597	747	1,483
Oceania	856	25	377	55	399
North and Central America	2,424	258	356	741	1,069
South America	1,776	72	291	902	511
Total	13,670	1,384	2,407	3,839	6,040
Per cent.	-	10·1	17·6	28·1	44·2

THE WORLD'S LANDS

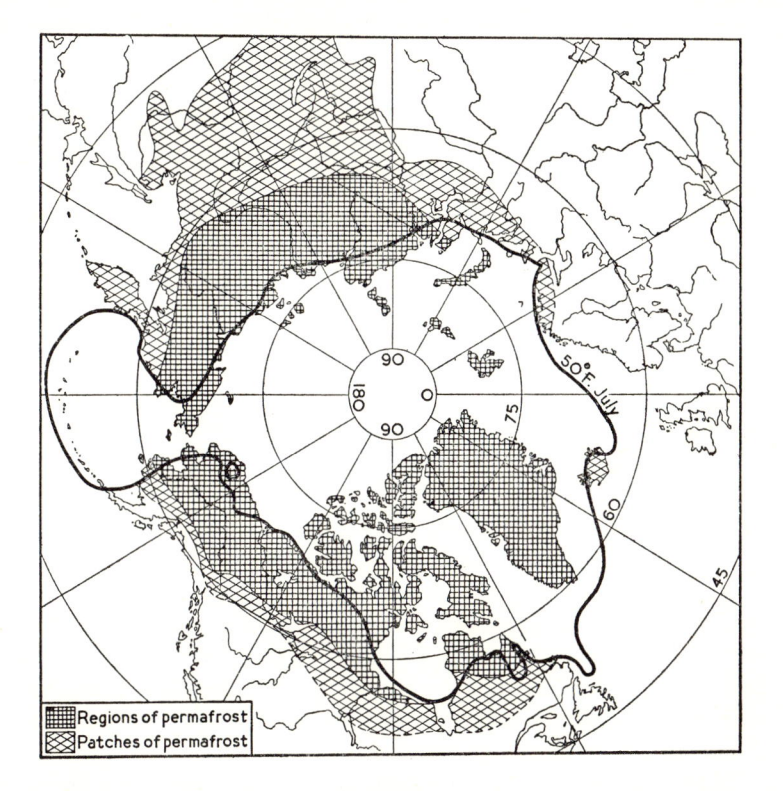

Fig. 19

The cold lands of the northern hemisphere. This map shows the ice-cap areas, where permanent settlement is obviously impossible, and the permafrost areas of permanently frozen subsoil where agriculture in the ordinarily accepted sense may be regarded as impossible; the same is true over most of the huge tracts where permafrost occurs in patches. Older authorities have regarded the July isotherm of 50° F. as marking the northern limit of possible cultivation. North of this line grazing on 'arctic prairies' by reindeer and other animals is possible, but only small populations could be supported.

This map, previously published in *Our Undeveloped World* (1953), was specially prepared by Professor F. Kenneth Hare, McGill University, Montreal, based on the work of Sumgin (U.S.S.R.), Müller (Alaska), Jenness (Canada west of Hudson Bay), and Hare (east of Hudson Bay).

THE WORLD'S LANDS
TABLE VI
WORLD LAND USE, 1959

Acres per head of population

	Total area	Arable or cropped	Permanent meadows and pastures	Forested land	Other land	Population (million)
Europe	3·0	0·9	0·5	0·8	0·7	420
U.S.S.R.	26·7	2·6	3·2	8·8	12·1	210
Asia	4·5	0·7	0·7	0·8	2·3	1,573
Africa	31·8	2·4	6·2	7·8	15·4	240
Oceania	125·8	3·6	55·4	8·1	58·7	17
North and Central America	23·6	2·5	3·5	7·2	10·4	256
South America	33·1	1·3	5·4	16·8	9·6	134
World	12·0	1·2	2·1	3·4	5·3	2,850

Excluding Antarctica

These tables reveal some very interesting facts. From Table V it will be seen that the area of arable or cropped land is very close to one-tenth, or 10 per cent, of the land surface. If one adds to this the 17·6 per cent of permanent pastures and meadows making allowance on the one hand for range land coming in this category but not having sufficient moisture for cultivation, and on the other hand for forest land which could be cleared and cultivated, one gets close to the 30 per cent of cultivable land already postulated.

Table VI affords several very useful world figures which can be used as yardsticks. In the first place there is 1·2 acre of arable or cropped land, including tree crops, per head of population. Making allowance for such non-food crops as cotton, jute and rubber, it takes the produce of roughly one acre, plus animal foodstuffs from grazing land, to feed one person. This is an 'average' with a tremendous range of foodstuffs, farming techniques, crop yields and standards of living. Even the crude figures given here, however, show how great are the contrasts between the continents.

Where are the Wide Open Spaces?

The next question is obviously how much of the land not at present cropped could be so used? A first approach is through consideration of the world's climates.

THE WORLD'S LANDS

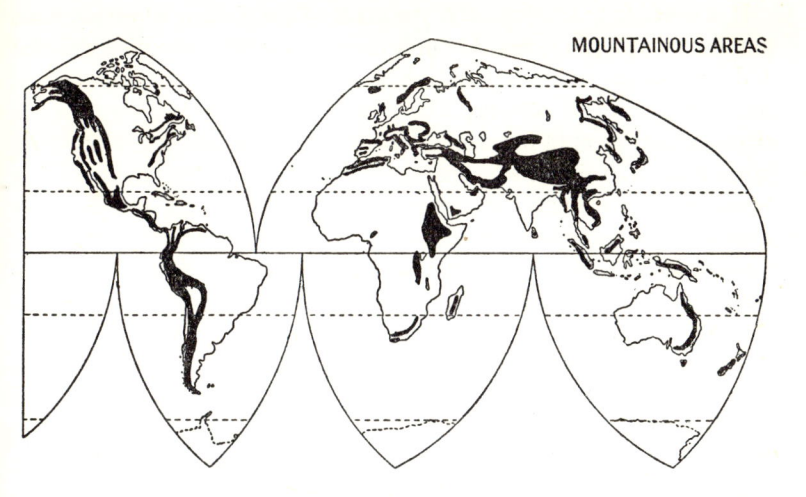

MOUNTAINOUS AREAS

Fig. 20

The main areas where the rugged or extremely elevated character of the surface prohibits close settlement are very roughly shown

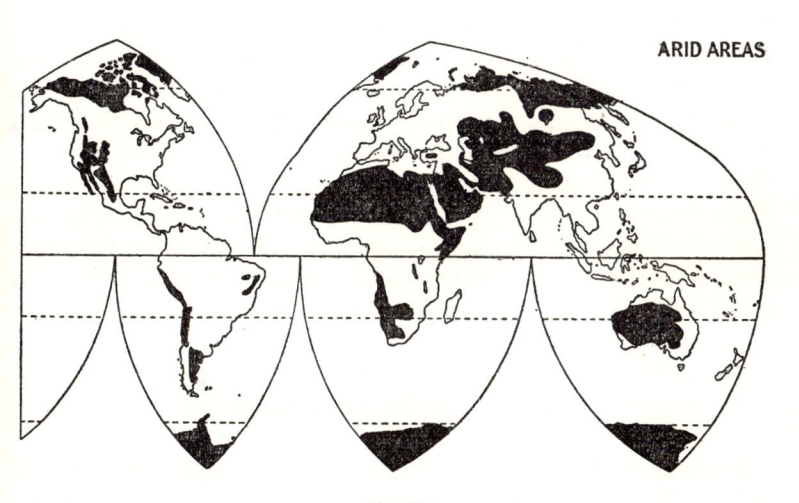

ARID AREAS

Fig. 21

This map shows where rainfall or other precipitation is too small to allow close agricultural settlement without irrigation. Roughly, the areas shown in black have less than 10 inches of rain or equivalent in snow in middle or high latitudes and less than 20 inches of rain in the tropics

THE WORLD'S LANDS

It is possible to separate over the lands of the globe a relatively small number of climatic types. About a dozen are commonly distinguished and it would seem that certain have favoured the settlement of man and the development of cultures. The lands round the Mediterranean Sea characterized by mild wet winters and hot dry summers and with a high proportion of available sunshine enjoy what has come to be known as a Mediterranean climate. It is not a climate which favours the easy weathering of rocks to form deep soil; it is not a climate which produces a particularly luxuriant vegetation since plants have to protect themselves against excessive loss of moisture in the long hot dry summer. Human beings find that same summer heat trying: they are almost compelled to rest during the heat of the midday hours. Yet it is a climate which has nurtured some of the greatest civilizations of all time—of Minos, Greece and Rome, as well as of the later development of Spain, Portugal and Italy. Where the same type of climate is found in other continents it has acted as a magnet to the incoming settlers—in California, central Chile, or the environs of Cape Town, Perth, Adelaide and Melbourne.

Similarly the tropical monsoon climate of south-east Asia has encouraged a vast multiplication of the human race. Yet, strangely enough, very similar climatic conditions over the tropical lands of Africa and South America have rarely encouraged dense populations. One can understand the absence of people from the arid lands—the great deserts —and from the cold forest and tundra lands. But why should so many parts of the well-watered tropics remain what Pierre Gourou has called forest deserts? It is almost true to say that the essentially underdeveloped lands, which appear to be capable of settlement and development, are those in the two major climatic regions of the tropics. It seems worth while therefore to examine in some detail these climates.

Climatic Regions of the World

A number of different classifications have been proposed for climatic regions.[1] Into these I shall not enter here; suffice it to say that for my

[1] See, for instance: C. W. Thornthwaite, 'Problems in the Classification of Climates', *Geographical Review*, XXXIII (1943), 233–55; id.: 'An Approach towards a Rational Classification of Climate', ibid., XXXVIII (1948), 55–94. Thornthwaite's own classification in its latest version, the key to which is the measurement of precipitation efficiency, involves a considerable amount of mathematical calculation, not easy for the laymen to understand.

THE WORLD'S LANDS

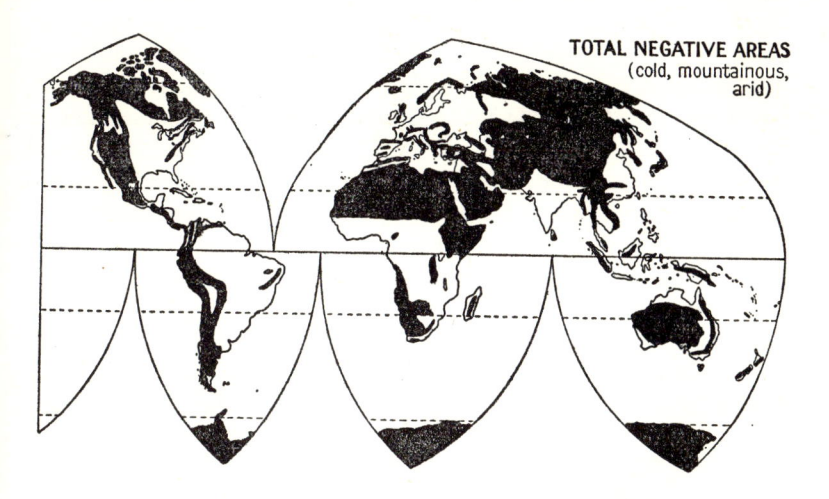

TOTAL NEGATIVE AREAS
(cold, mountainous, arid)

Fig. 22

The map combines Figs. 19, 20 and 21 and shows those parts of the earth's surface which through cold, aridity, or mountainous character prohibit close settlement and agricultural development. It does not take account of irrigation settlements where the 'negative' character of the land has been counteracted, notably in Egypt, Iraq, north-western India and western Pakistan, Russian Central Asia, and parts of western United States.

The blank areas which remain on this map are potentially cultivable or actually cultivated. Although so much of the earth's surface has been eliminated, many areas have been given the benefit of the doubt in deciding whether or not they are 'cultivable': thus the high plateau of Bolivia, a considerable part of the Canadian Shield, Finland and the Russian forest lands are included.

The map serves to focus attention on the 'positive' or presumably developable areas of South America and Africa as the major under-developed lands, and calls attention to comparable problems of Canada and U.S.S.R. in northward expansion.

present purpose I make use primarily of the classification of Finch and Trewartha in the slightly modified form in which it appears in the *Army Service Forces Manual M 101*. This classification has the advantage of being in close agreement with Professor A. J. Herbertson's well-known regional scheme. As will be seen by a comparison of Figs. 23 and 24, Finch and Trewartha's Type A1, Tropical Rain-forest, is the same as Herbertson's Equatorial, but has been extended by Type 1t to include the wettest parts of the Tropical Climate of Herbertson and by 1m to include the wettest parts of Tropical Monsoon lands. Type A2, Tropical Savanna, is the same as Herbertson's Tropical together with Tropical Monsoon of India and south-east Asia, and so Types 1 and 2 of Finch and Trewartha are particularly the 'under-developed' areas with which we are concerned.

It will be noted that both Herbertson's scheme and that of Finch and Trewartha take note of the very close link between climate and vegetation. Indeed the climatic types are often named from the characteristic vegetation. When climatologists such as Köppen and Thornthwaite attempt to define more exactly the climatic limits they produce classifications which are more artificial in the sense that they do not coincide so closely with the observed distribution of vegetation types.

Equatorial Climate or Tropical Rain-forest

As its name implies, this is the type of climate normally found as a belt stretching some five to ten degrees on either side af the Equator. It is the region where constant heat throughout the year results in continuous evaporation, upward movement of air currents, and local rather than regional winds. Temperatures are not extreme; over huge areas the thermometer rarely drops below 70° F. and rarely rises above 90° F. The mean for every day of the year is not far from 80° F. Just as monotony is the keynote of temperature, so it is of rainfall. in many parts the early morning mist suggests a coolness more apparent than real, and the mist is soon dispersed by morning sunshine. Evaporation is rapid, ascending air currents frequently result in the formation of clouds in the afternoon, followed by a heavy downpour of rain, the sky clearing again in the late evening.

Such a daily régime may be repeated almost without variation throughout the year, though in some places one season may be wetter than another and in other places a double rainfall maximum in the course of the year is normal. The rainfall is always adequate—80 inches a year is a typical average—and always in marked excess of evaporation, and is not subject to violent fluctuations from year to year.

The keynote of the equatorial climate is thus a combination of heat and moisture and an absence of seasonal rhythm. These conditions are reflected in the natural vegetation, typically a lofty, evergreen forest. Individual trees may and do have their resting periods and may shed their leaves, but there is no period when the forest as a whole displays the typical features of a resting period such as that in the deciduous forest of mid-latitudes. Heat and moisture induce continuous and easy growth, trees grow tall and unbranched in their struggle for existence; other plants have adopted the habits of woody climbers and epiphytes, living high up on the supporting trees. Much of the animal life of these forests also is concentrated in the tree-tops. By contrast the floor of the forest is commonly in perpetual gloom, littered with a debris of fallen leaves which decay with a damp, fetid odour rather than change to the humus associated with mid-latitudes.

Over huge areas the equatorial lands are scarcely to be described as under-developed. They are literally undeveloped and largely uninhabited. At first sight this may seem difficult to explain. In a wood-hungry world, why should these forests which afford the largest stretches of unworked timber land, have remained so little exploited? The trees are of many different species; the majority, though not all, are hardwoods of the type known technically as 'tropical cabinet woods'. These are of somewhat limited use; indeed less than 2 per cent of the timber consumed in the world is to be described under the general title of tropical hardwood. Each wood is distinctive and while there is a commercial demand for a few types, it is difficult to establish a demand for all. Consequently, in exploitation, the alternatives are clear felling of the forest with the difficulty of finding a market or indeed a use for the many and varied types of timber, or selective felling of the commercially valuable trees, a virtually impossible task.

Since we are chiefly concerned at this time with the provision of food for the growing human family, we should perhaps look at the equatorial forest from the point of view of the value of the cleared land.

The admittedly luxuriant growth of the giant trees has led to some false assessments of the value of the land when cleared. The deduction that the soil must be inherently fertile has proved repeatedly to be far from the truth. With rainfall always in excess of evaporation, there is a net downward movement of water in the soil. That is to say there is

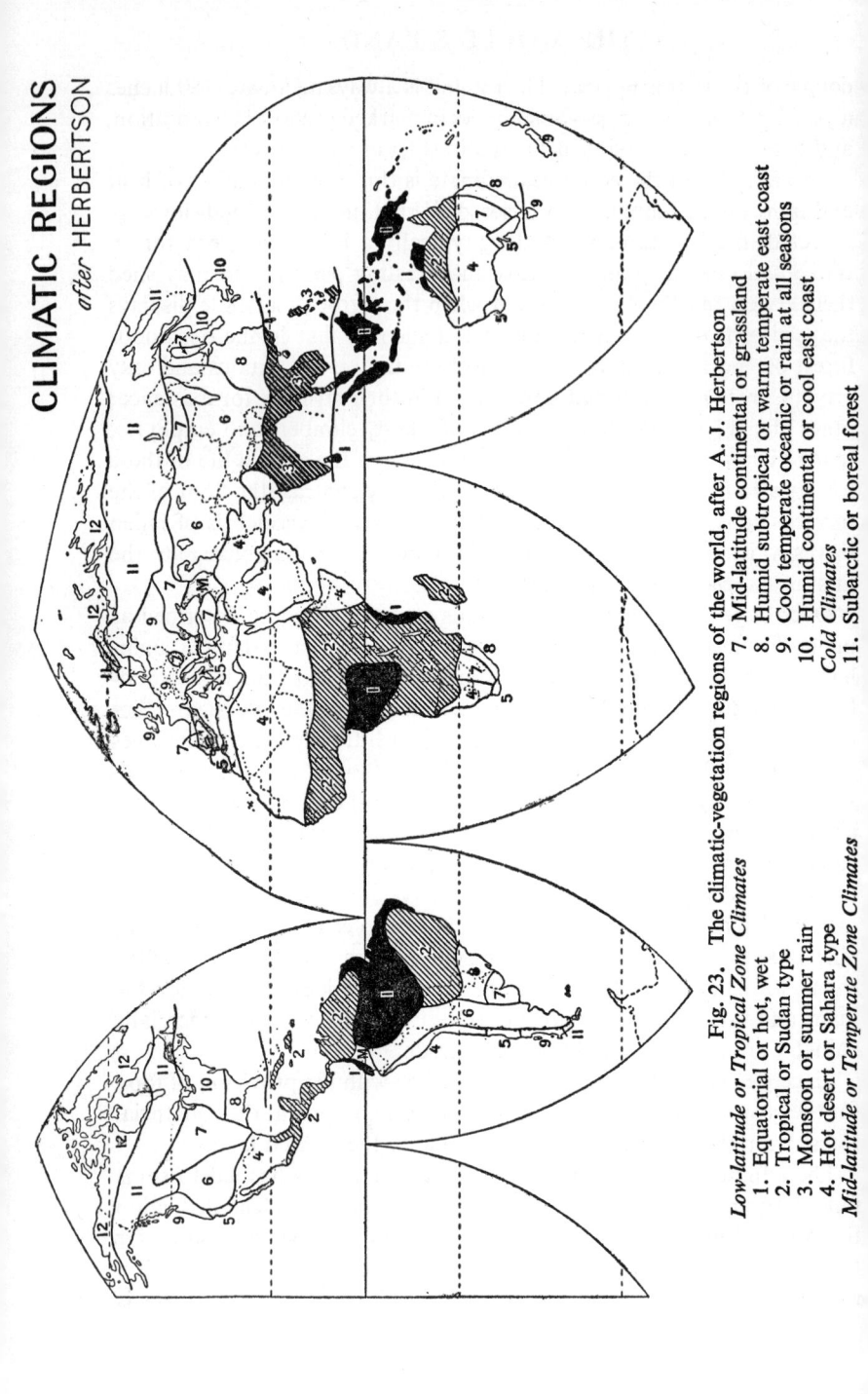

Fig. 23. The climatic-vegetation regions of the world, after A. J. Herbertson

Low-latitude or Tropical Zone Climates
1. Equatorial or hot, wet
2. Tropical or Sudan type
3. Monsoon or summer rain
4. Hot desert or Sahara type

Mid-latitude or Temperate Zone Climates

7. Mid-latitude continental or grassland
8. Humid subtropical or warm temperate east coast
9. Cool temperate oceanic or rain at all seasons
10. Humid continental or cool east coast

Cold Climates
11. Subarctic or boreal forest

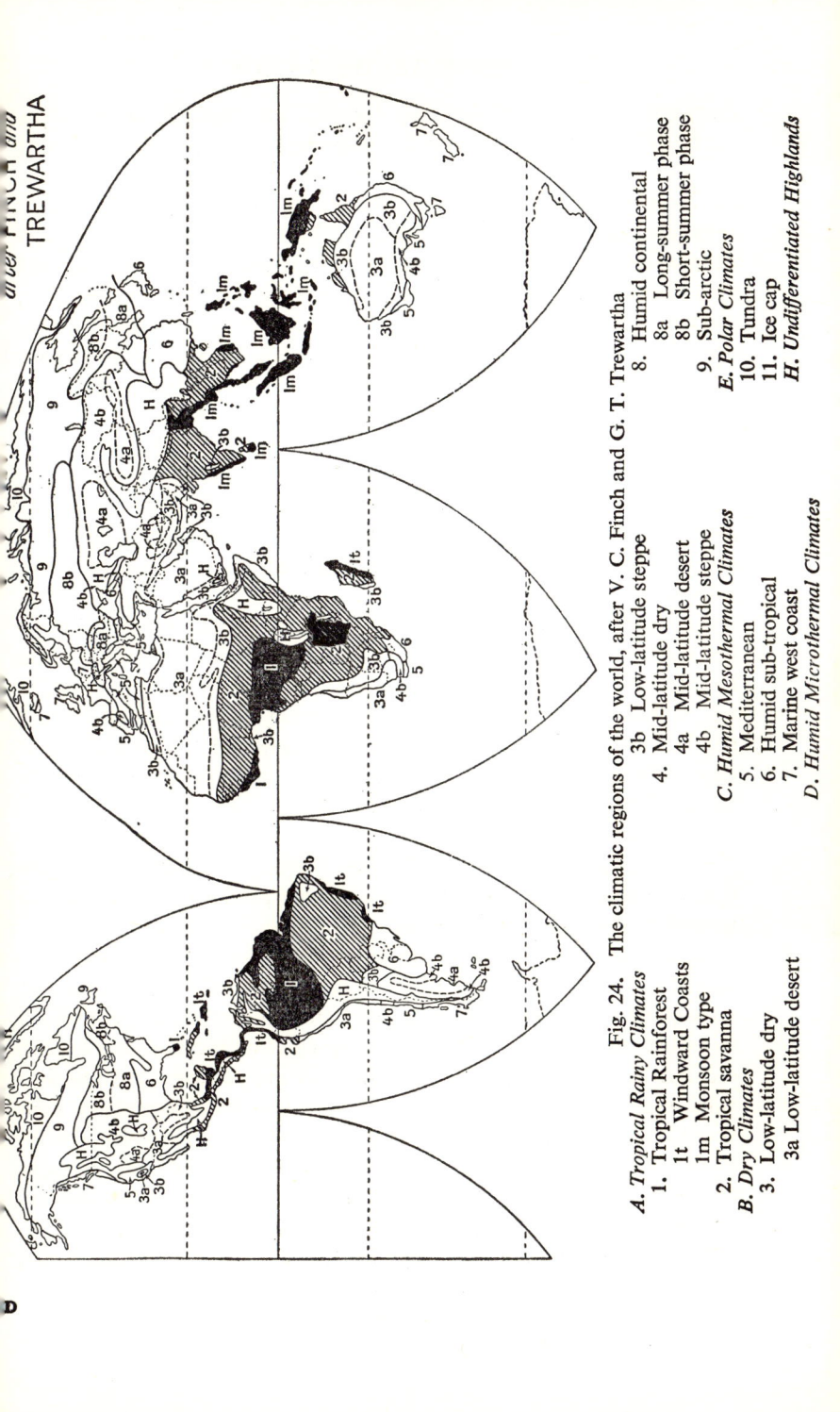

Fig. 24. The climatic regions of the world, after V. C. Finch and G. T. Trewartha

A. Tropical Rainy Climates
1. Tropical Rainforest
    1t Windward Coasts
    1m Monsoon type
2. Tropical savanna

B. Dry Climates
3. Low-latitude dry
    3a Low-latitude desert
    3b Low-latitude steppe
4. Mid-latitude dry
    4a Mid-latitude desert
    4b Mid-latitude steppe

C. Humid Mesothermal Climates
5. Mediterranean
6. Humid sub-tropical
7. Marine west coast

D. Humid Microthermal Climates
8. Humid continental
    8a Long-summer phase
    8b Short-summer phase
9. Sub-arctic

E. Polar Climates
10. Tundra
11. Ice cap

H. Undifferentiated Highlands

downward leaching which, when the soils are exposed, tends to impoverish the surface layers and to sweep plant food downwards, leaving the surface a sterile mixture of mineral particles. At the same time when the forest is cleared and the soil exposed, the high temperatures induce rapid chemical action, notably rapid oxidation. The resultant impoverishment of the soil is increased rapidly by the process of ploughing. We may literally say, as was proved from experiments many years ago in Ceylon, that the goodness can be ploughed out of the soil in a very short time. By and large, if cleared, the equatorial forests would provide vast areas of poor or indifferent soils, liable to become still further impoverished, and further liable to marked soil erosion.

The old myth that equatorial soils are of great fertility dies hard. Early writers on Ceylon, for example J. W. Bennett in *Ceylon and its Capabilities* (1843), refer repeatedly to its 'fertile soil', 'pre-eminent in natural resources'; but Sir Samuel Baker, in a work we shall have occasion to mention later, speaks of his disillusionment as a pioneer of 1848 when he says:[1]

'The appearance of the (soil) has deceived everyone, especially the black soil of the patina, which my bailiff on his first arrival declared to be excellent. Lord Torrington, who is well known as an agriculturalist, was equally deceived. He was very confident in the opinion that "it only required draining to enable it to produce anything". The real fact is that it will not pay for the working.... In fact, nothing will permanently succeed in Ceylon soil without abundance of manure, with the exception of cinnamon and coco-nuts....

'Can any man when describing the "fertility" of Ceylon be aware that ... newly-cleared forest land will only produce one crop of the miserable grain called *korrakan*.'

Going back much further, the Amazon basin was the reputed location of El Dorado. Carvajal, who accompanied Orellana on his pioneer journey down its main stream in the sixteenth century, felt compelled to write enthusiastically of the imaginary cities he had hoped to see but did not find. Yet apparently his accounts are accepted at their face value even today by some writers; at least this is the impression conveyed by Earl Parker Hanson in his *New Worlds Emerging* (1950). Even if we accept these old accounts as literally true, the fact remains that Nature has proved the master and destroyed former settlements and civilizations almost without trace.

Two phrases that have been applied to the hot, wet equatorial lands

[1] Sir Samuel Baker, *Eight Years in Ceylon* (London, 1855), pp. 53–8.

are pregnant with meaning. Professor H. J. Fleure described them as 'regions of lasting difficulty', where man was in a state of constant struggle against the natural climatic factors. The second phase rightly describes the equatorial climate as a 'good servant but a bad master'.

So far we have referred to the equatorial belt in broad terms; actually there are great contrasts between its different parts. In vast stretches of Amazonian forest small groups of aboriginal tribes eke out a precarious existence, partly by living on or along the waterways and combining fishing with hunting and the gathering of fruits and roots. In the Congo forests there are still primitive groups which emulate the wild animals by living in dwellings in the trees themselves. On the other hand in some parts, perhaps best exemplified on the margins of the true equatorial belt in Africa, man has succeeded in modifying his environment to some extent. On patches of cleared land where, in part by reason of their small size, soil erosion is kept in check, yams and other vegetables and bananas and other fruits are grown. It is in some of these areas that the cash crop of cocoa has been introduced, as well as the oil palm, and there are other products of interest in international trade such as sago and tapioca.

Then there are equatorial areas where man can claim to be master. We think particularly of Java and certain of the favoured parts of the East Indies and of the Malayan Peninsula. The food crop of paramount importance is rice, and we notice at once that its cultivation demands special soil conditions: the soil must be such, clay for example, that it can be worked into a water-holding layer, and the land must either be flat or susceptible to terracing. In Java these conditions are not only fulfilled over considerable areas, but the volcanic soils widespread in the island have a naturally high nutrient status. The developed parts of south-east Asia are also favoured by such local modifications that the climate is not typically equatorial. Monsoonal conditions exist, and the seasonal winds, the land and sea breezes, and the varied relief result in pronounced local differences.

The non-food crop which has meant so much to the development of these lands is the introduced *Hevea braziliensis*, the rubber tree, and the modern rubber plantations illustrate well the precautions needed when dealing with equatorial lands. It is unwise to clear extensive areas of hillside—great scars all too frequently evidence the danger of exposing the soil to erosion. Even the gently sloping lowlands must be treated with caution. When the forest is cleared, the stumps of the trees are usually left, the roots helping to bind the soil together, and each little rubber tree is rimmed around to prevent rapid run off; or more commonly the ground is immediately protected by a cover crop, and one which will add to its nutrient status. Protect the soil, keep it covered, is the universal rule in these lands.

However, examined in detail, the conquest of these more favoured equatorial lands is far from complete. Less than one-sixth of Malaya, for instance, is under cultivation—food and plantation crops. The cleared valleys and lowlands are separated by large stretches of forest that vie with any in the world for impenetrability.

We may summarize the position in the equatorial lands by saying that the maps suggest that there are at least a couple of million square miles of under-developed or undeveloped land; but the difficulties of bringing them into use are enormous and are likely to remain enormous. There is first the difficulty of clearing the land. There is then the difficulty of conserving and building up the soils—a wholly new technique of soil management needs to be developed. Although some important advances are being made, the British expert committee on problems of mechanization,[1] reporting in 1949, failed to reach definite conclusions. The third difficulty is the lack of population. While the old idea that these hot, wet lands are unhealthy by reason of their climate is no longer to be accepted in its crude form, the climate does present serious obstacles. Its monotony is incompatible with the normal rhythm of life with its alternating periods of rest and activity. We sum this up by saying that when a man gets run down or below par, recovery is difficult without a change of climate. Further, though the climate itself may not be 'unhealthy' there are many widespread diseases—such as malaria, dengue and other fevers, dysentery and digestive troubles—which take their toll, if not of life, certainly of efficiency.

What are the products to be obtained from equatorial lands? Undoubtedly the chief is rice, but the swing of the world's people, even in those countries where it is grown, is away from rice consumption to the cereals of mid-latitudes, which at present at least cannot be produced in the hot, wet lands. In so far as these under-developed lands can produce a surplus for export, what should that surplus be?

Some new and alarming pests and diseases of plants have appeared. The recent spread of the swollen shoot disease which threatened for a time to extirpate the cocoa trees and the cocoa industry in West Africa

[1] 'Report of a Survey of Problems in the Mechanization of Native Agriculture in Tropical African Colonies', *Colonial Advisory Council of Agriculture, Animal Health and Forestry*, No. 1, 1950.

(though it is now believed to be under control) is an illustration of the disasters besetting development in equatorial lands.

Vast tracts of the equatorial lands may be listed for possible future development, but sober appraisal will insist that the development cannot be undertaken until far more is known of ways to go about it. An appreciation of this fact was UNESCO's efforts to create the Hylea Research Institute in equatorial Brazil. The establishment of an agronomic institute for the Belgian Congo (INEAC), with its central field station at Yangambi, is another example of the growth of scientific research in an equatorial land. And most significant for African development are the regular conferences now held by workers in such fields as soils, agronomy, and land use on a pan-African basis.[1] On still broader lines was the first African Regional Scientific Conference which met at Johannesburg in 1949. The conference passed a resolution creating a Scientific Council for Africa south of the Sahara[2] and this was implemented shortly afterwards.

Since then much important scientific work has been carried on in equatorial and tropical lands. In addition to C.S.A. (Conseil Scientifique pour l'Afrique au Sud du Sahara) as the body just mentioned is usually called, C.C.T.A. (Commission de Coopération Technique en Afrique au Sud du Sahara) was set up in January 1950, and was the subject of an inter-governmental agreement signed in London in January 1954, and now has eight member governments with an object to 'ensure technical co-operation between territories for which member governments are responsible in Africa south of the Sahara'. C.S.A. and C.C.T.A. have a joint secretariat with offices in London and Bukavu and a large number of publications have now been issued.

UNESCO, in addition to its Arid Zone programme, initiated an extensive programme of work on the Humid Tropics. To assist the investigators other international organizations are collaborating. For example the International Geographical Union with over forty member countries set up an official Standing Commission on the Humid Tropics.

All this should serve to indicate that the eyes of the world are now

[1] See *inter alia* the 'Reports of Conferences' at Yangambi (Semaine Agricole de Yangambi, *Institut National pour l'Etude Agronomique du Congo Belge*, Pts. I and II, 1947), at Goma (*Bulletin Agricole du Congo Belge*, Pts. I, II, III, 1949), and Jos (British African Land Utilization Conference, Jos, Nigeria, Nov. 1949; *Final Report* printed in Zaria, Nigeria, for the Conference).

[2] Th. Monod, 'Two African International Scientific Conferences,' *Geographical Review*, XL (1950), 309–12.

being focused on the relatively undeveloped tropics, both the very wet equatorial regions and the drier Savanna lands now to be discussed.

The Tropical Climate or Tropical Savanna

We may understand by the term 'tropical climate' that which occurs outside the equatorial belt but still within the tropics. It is marked by a distinctive seasonal rhythm, in which it is usual to distinguish three seasons. There is the cool dry season, 'cool' having however a relative meaning in that the thermometer does not sink below the crucial 43° F., the temperature below which the majority of plants of economic importance cease to be vegetatively active. In general this season, in the northern hemisphere from late October through January to February, is one of sunny skies and, over large areas, of cool constant winds, since this is the Trade Wind belt. The cool dry season passes gradually into the hot dry season. The land heats up, temperatures by day and night rise, air movement becomes less marked, rain is absent, everything becomes dry and parched. Towards the end of this season many native trees and shrubs, seemingly able to anticipate the coming of the rains, burst into flower before pollination is inhibited. The third season is the hot wet period, often called the rains, from about the end of May or June through September into October, a season when rains are heavy though sometimes spasmodic in their occurrence. It will be noticed that because the rains coincide with what in mid-latitudes would be called the summer, vegetative growth is very active in common with chemical action in the soils.

Though we refer to the tropical climate we might more correctly talk about the tropical climates, in that there is a wide range from the wet margins bordering on equatorial lands where the 'dry' season is dry by comparison rather than in actuality, to the arid margins which fade into the great deserts, where the total rainfall for the year is 20 inches or less. These great variations are reflected in the natural vegetation. On the wet equatorial margins the rainfall, though it may be mainly in the one season, is sufficiently heavy (80 inches or more) to maintain the growth of an evergreen forest similar to that of the equatorial lands themselves. Over the vast extent of the tropical lands, however, the vegetation is that variously described as savanna, parkland, orchard-bush, grassland with scattered trees, or locally by such names as campos (Brazil), llanos (Venezuela) and scrub forest.

THE WORLD'S LANDS

The tropical climate is *par excellence* the climate of Africa. Over vast stretches are grasslands with scattered trees, such as various species of acacia and the well-known baobab, which merge into actual forests where water conditions improve, as in the so-called gallery forests along the river valleys. Where conditions are more arid, the trees—often of the same species—become spiny bushes, and there is a natural transition into thorn scrub. Over certain tracts trees and shrubs may be entirely absent; but it would be wrong to think of these vast stretches of grassland in terms of those familiar in mid-latitudes. Tropical grasses not infrequently reach 8 and 10 feet in height.

Of all the under-developed or undeveloped lands in the world the tropical savannas call most urgently for careful study. The term grassland suggests natural pastures awaiting the herdsman. This was what the Spaniards thought when they introduced European cattle into the llanos of the Orinoco basin three centuries ago. How is it that with all the developments in the New World so little use has yet been made of the vast South American pasture lands?

For a first explanation, let us follow the fate of a herd of cattle through the year. The end of a dry season of six to eight months finds them completely exhausted from the constant effort to find water and nutriment in the vast stretches of parched and dried-up grassland. With the first coming of the rains the grass roots spring into life, fodder becomes abundant, and those cattle still able to stand find plenty of sustenance, though of course the rains may be delayed, and more animals succumb; and doubtless some overeat and die as a result of the new abundance. For a few weeks the food supply is satisfactory, but so rapid is the vegetative growth that the grasses quickly become tough and lose their palatability and some of their nutritive value. If the rains are heavy, the herd may be in danger of drowning, and will have difficulty in finding patches of dry land and spots where young and palatable fodder still exists. The rains last for two or three months, and then the cycle starts over again. We may sum it up by saying that from the point of view of cattle-rearing, the favourable season is about two months out of the twelve.

What then of cultivation? Tropical soils present many problems. In the rainy season heat and moisture combine to cause downward leaching so long as rainfall exceeds evaporation. With the coming of the dry season, the movement of soil moisture is reversed, evaporation exceeds rainfall, the evaporating moisture leaves behind in the soil the salts contained in solution, with the result that a hardpan may be formed at

THE WORLD'S LANDS

or near the surface. The hardpan in its turn prevents both proper circulation of water in the soil and the penetration of roots. The net result is that tropical soils call for a completely different system of management from that used in mid-latitudes.

To the catalogue of difficulties must be added rainfall variability, which is particularly marked in the drier parts of the tropical lands. An average rainfall of 20 to 30 inches may be adequate for arable cultivation, but when this average is in fact derived from extremes of 10 inches one year and 40 to 50 the next, the famine of the one year resulting from drought is matched by the famine of the next year resulting from excessive rainfall. Control of water supplies, whether for cultivation or for watering of stock, is priority No. 1 in all tropical lands.

In many parts of tropical Africa rainfall variability from year to year both in the coming of the rains and in the total amount—is particularly marked. Over the great plateau surfaces of Africa there are no mountain ranges to act as climatic divides as there are in other continents. Rain is associated with the meeting of air masses, especially along the so-called ITCZ (Inter-tropical Convergence Zone) which may vary widely in position. Even in coastal stations, as the following figures for Bathurst (over an 18-year period) show, the variation is very great.

	May	June	July	August	Sept.	Oct.	Nov.	
Max.	1·90	12·32	13·93	19·56	13·08	9·08	0·20	inches
Min.	0·00	2·24	5·10	6·79	5·78	0·24	0·00	,,

In any given year deficiencies in one month may be made up in another —often, however, with a disastrous effect on crops—but even yearly totals show a range over the same 18-year period from 23·68 to 56·07 inches, with an average of 43·36. If we regard 40 inches as the 'safety line', this is how the eighteen years, 1902–18, worked out:

```
                              1910
        45    57   66 64    44 57 44         49   48   54
    40 ─────────────────────────────────────────────────── 40
             29   38    34         28 34 24   38   38
```

The sequence of three bad years is particularly noteworthy, especially when one remembers that evaporation in these latitudes is at least equivalent to 20 inches of rain. It is worse still in the interior.

THE WORLD'S LANDS

Taming the Tropics

Although the map shows vast areas of the tropics sparsely populated, it is abundantly clear that even if there are still these wide open spaces, many problems remain to be solved, and success is by no means assured.[1]

The East African Ground-nut scheme was a great gamble. It might have been a tremendous success. It is quoted here merely to show how much is still to be learned. Eventually man will come to understand the tropical climate and its effects on soil, vegetation and crops and will devise techniques of land management accordingly. At present our techniques are inadequate, perhaps even diametrically wrong. We still need to know, perhaps to evolve, the right agricultural implements—quite possibly the plough should not be used at all in tropical lands—we need effective control of water-supply and plant nutrients, we need to produce new plants—particularly nutritious grasses and fodder crops which will overcome both the dangers of surface soil erosion and the formation of sub-surface hardpan, and which will maintain a fodder supply throughout the year, we need much additional knowledge as to food crops which can be grown and will maintain an adequate basis of human nutrition which some diets—for example in Africa—fail to do at present.[2]

There will be many more disappointments and failures. The boldly planned experiment in Queensland for growing sorghum millet coupled with pig-raising was not by any means a complete success; the Government-sponsored poultry farming scheme for smallholders in the Gambia has to be recognized as a failure. It is worth quoting from a London *Times* editorial on this subject:[3]

'The forces of Nature are strong in the tropics and the conversion of bush into productive farming land is more than a task for bulldozers. The soil and its defects have to be closely studied. Usually there are good reasons why the natives have left the bush to Nature. The time for bold investment is when scientists and agriculturalists can diagnose the deficiencies and advise with some assurance on how they can be met.'

These experiments of ten years ago already belong to history. Every-

---

[1] For a general assessment see D. H. K. Lee, *Climate and Economic Development in the Tropics*, New York, Harper, 1957.

[2] See *inter alia The State of Food and Agriculture*, 1958, Rome, FAO, 1958, 90 et seq.

The Times Weekly Edition, London, 14th March 1951.

THE WORLD'S LANDS

where there is an active spirit of scientific inquiry. A pioneer investigation of great interest which may be quoted as an example of many was that carried out in the Gambia by a team of medical and nutrition experts working with agriculturalists at the village of Geneiri, 150 miles up the river from the coast. Climatically Geneiri is on the drier margin of the tropical belt. It has been described as having no average rainfall and no average temperature, but rainfall is of the character shown for Bathurst on p. 56.

Geneiri exists on subsistence agriculture, some 80 per cent of the villagers' diet consisting of cereals. Interestingly enough, no less than four or even five cereals enter into the diet, chiefly because the harvest is thereby spread over some five or six months of the year from late July or mid-August when maize is available, to January or early February, when the last of the rice is harvested. Maize is followed by sorghum, then by *Pennisetum* (bulrush millet) and finally by *Digitaria* (finger grass) and rice. The remainder of the diet is from leafy vegetables such as okra, occasional fish and, on rare occasions, chicken, goat or beef. The people are poor farmers. All work is by hand, and out of the 2,000-acre area proper to the village, perhaps a couple of hundred acres are cultivated, probably the limit of which they are physically capable.

As a result existence is essentially from hand to mouth. The food is eaten as produced. It has been rightly said that the human body is there submitted twice a year to opposite types of maltreatment: too much food for a short season with consequent digestive troubles, too little food in the dry season, the so-called 'hungry season', with consequent recurrent famine oedema. Malnutrition is apparent in the physical appearance and weight of the villagers. In July when they were well fed the average weight of the adults was 130 lb.; in the following dry season the average weight had dropped to 120 lb., this just at a time when physical energy was needed to prepare the land for the new crop. With the introduction of new food supplies weight increased. The experimenters, by importing food, succeeded after two seasons (1947–49) in maintaining the average weight and indeed increasing it to 139 lb. over the period July 1947 to April 1949. It was found, however, as in the case of the good feeding of African troops, that the effects of malnutrition during early years could not be completely eliminated by diet in adolescents and adults. This last point is highly significant; it means that a generation or more must pass before the general level of health and stamina can be built up; it underlines the impossibility of rapid development in tropical lands.

THE WORLD'S LANDS

On the agricultural side the group carried out three parallel experiments: the encouragement of native agriculture; experimental farming with modern machinery on selected blocks of land cleared for the purpose; and a partnership under an arrangement whereby the village shared the produce. In addition to encouraging the growth of cereals, the further cultivation of ground-nuts as a cash crop was promoted. The Africans, working by hand, obtained a maximum production of 250 lb. of ground-nuts per acre, with plants rather widely spaced. By introducing full-scale mechanical cultivation (a Fordson tractor and a Ferguson tractor being used with both disc ploughs and light steel ploughs, seed sown mechanically, etc.) it was found possible to treble the number of plants per acre to 50,000 and so to step up the production to a maximum of 900 lb. per acre.

At first sight this would seem to be satisfactory, but although the number of plants per acre was increased and hence the production speeded up, the yield per plant remained low and the plants appeared to be suffering from some deficiency disease not understood. Strip cropping was adopted to prevent soil erosion, but the formation of hardpan and the difficulties of proper drainage, combined with aeration of the soil, have not yet been overcome. Presuming the equipment to be supplied free of capital cost, the financial results of the experiment when carried out co-operatively with the Africans showed at the end a profit of about one shilling per day per labourer. This is half the normal local wage of labour employed by the day in the area.

In the meantime, by establishment of medical services, general health conditions had been greatly improved. The villagers expressed their appreciation of their contacts with Western civilization by saying: 'Before our babies die, now they live.' And thus we come back once again to the crucial question of the increasing pressure on the land. The Gambia experiment shows how many are the difficulties still to be overcome in the development of tropical lands, even with all the skill and the implements available to us.

Water Control and Irrigation in the Tropics

If variability of rainfall from year to year is the greatest single difficulty in the development of tropical lands, it follows almost automatically that the control of water-supplies is the first need in most of those lands. Where the rain is heavy, there must be control to help run-off without causing soil erosion and to prevent disastrous flooding, but to permit adequate flooding of rice fields. Where rainfall is moderate, water control is needed as insurance against bad seasons and still more to provide for the dry season—'the hungry season' of Africa—and thus to permit a wider range of crops and longer growing period and extended harvests. Where rainfall is scanty this becomes even more necessary; where rainfall is both small and unreliable, irrigation is vital to settlement and development.

That the Nile is the life-blood of Egypt is well known. That British-Indian government irrigation schemes have added to the productive lands of India and Pakistan many times the area of Egypt is less often appreciated. At the present time the great Owen Falls works where the Nile leaves Lake Victoria and the Kariba Gorge dam on the Zambezi between Northern and Southern Rhodesia are two examples from under-developed Africa of bold schemes that combine water control with power development.

Reviewing the problem in tropical Africa, Professor Frank Debenham[1] has urged that, ideally, no water at all should be allowed to escape to the oceans—it is all needed for agriculture. In contrast to the great hydro-electric and irrigation schemes that have been proposed, he considers that Africans could be taught to do much to help themselves. He advocates control of run-off and temporary storage of water by erecting earth dams across small valleys and piping supplies to villages for domestic needs and to fields for watering cattle; and the use of falling water for grinding mills to save much of the drudgery in the life of African women and release their energies for other purposes. Where circumstances are favourable—which is only locally the case in Africa—water is best stored underground, where both contamination and loss by evaporation are minimized and the water can be reached by wells. In contrast to the peoples of India and many other countries, the African is little accustomed to the use of wells. Such simple methods extend the availability of water-supplies and cut down the 'hungry season', eliminate much of the wasted labour in fetching supplies and lower the prevalence of disease resulting from contaminated water.

In hot, dry lands, especially when swept by wind, water in the soil evaporates quickly, leaving behind contained salts. Irrigation schemes

[1] Frank Debenham, 'Report on the Water Resources of the Bechuanaland Protectorate, Northern Rhodesia, the Nyasaland Protectorate, Tanganyika Territory, Kenya and the Uganda Protectorate.' *Colonial Research Publications*, No. 2, 1948.

may be outstandingly successful for a few years, but then accumulation of alkaline salts in the surface layers of the soil begins to affect cultivation. Enough flowing water to wash salts out of the soil is needed—a delicate balance must be maintained. Anyone who has flown over irrigated northern India will have noticed what appears from the air to be an attack of measles or some skin disease of the land. This is the first danger signal of increasing alkalinity and it is not so easily seen on the ground as from the air. Dr. H. L. Hoskins, writing on 'Point IV with Reference to the Middle East',[1] believes the abandonment of old irrigation settlements in Iran, Iraq and elsewhere in the Middle East to be due to alkalinity. He quotes a modern case: 'The famed Al Kharj oasis in Saudi Arabia. . . . Here in a two-thousand acre tract is the model farm of King Ibn-Saud. Under the direction of an American agricultural expert and staff and financed by the King's oil royalties, experiments are undertaken in the development of food and forage plants adapted to the Arabian environment. From the horticultural point of view the undertaking has been a distinct success, but in another respect it is probably doomed to eventual failure. The tract is watered from a deep natural reservoir, whose waters are hardly potable. Every irrigation channel is rimmed with alkaline salts. . . . From year to year as new sections are put to the plough, others must be abandoned as no longer productive.'

Mid-Latitude Comparisons

I have devoted considerable space to the consideration of the equatorial and tropical climates because these include the most important of the under-developed or undeveloped lands of the world. When we turn for purposes of comparison to the middle latitudes, those familiar to us in the United States or in Europe, we are reminded at once of the relative kindliness of Nature in providing climatic conditions more directly suited to the production of man's principal food crops. We shall examine later conditions in the British Isles, but in passing we may repeat the statement that for many farming purposes climatic conditions common to north-western Europe are ideal. With an average temperature in the coldest month above 32° F. it is never too cold for

[1] In 'Aiding Underdeveloped Areas Abroad', *Annals of The American Academy of Political and Social Science*, CCLXVIII (1950), 85–95; ref. on p. 88. See also Douglas D. Crary, 'Recent Agricultural Developments in Saudi Arabia', *Geographica Review*, XLI, 1951, 366–83.

outdoor farming operations; with an average temperature in the hottest month between 55° and 72° or 73° F. it is never too hot in the summer for outdoor occupations. The seasonal rhythm of summer and winter is such as to produce a welcome resting period, but a long period of vegetative growth. The climate certainly is ideal for grass and other fodder crops. The precipitation, mainly as rain, coming in almost equal amounts in each of the months throughout the year, keeps the land green and fertile, and rarely is water-supply a source of real anxiety. In the drier parts of these lands summer sunshine is adequate for ripening of grain.

Let us transfer the picture to the mid-latitude continental climate, that of the heart of the United States and Canada, where colder winters provide a longer resting period, where frost helps the farmer's plough in breaking up the heavier soils and in destroying some of the pests which might otherwise survive. The summers have adequate warmth and sunshine to provide excellent ripening conditions for cereal crops, conditions not far from ideal from the point of view of the cereal farmer.

If we may jump ahead to an obvious conclusion which I shall later endeavour to substantiate, it is that there are greater immediate prospects of increasing agricultural output in the middle latitudes than there is of securing immediate help in the world food situation from the much more difficult tropical lands. In other words, we shall be looking for the under-developed areas at least as much in our familiar middle latitudes as we shall be in the doubtful El Dorados of the tropics.

A Russian View

West European and American workers seeking a broad natural classification of the regions of the world have looked especially to climate, with or without a consideration of natural vegetation. It was left to Russian workers to develop another basic approach—that of soil. Over the vast monotonous plains which make up so much of the Russian lands climate has wrought its work on what is geologically a relatively homogeneous surface layer; climatic differences are reflected in soil differences. So there came the concept of the great world groups of soils, each with certain range of natural vegetation and each to be conceived as having a permissible range of economic crops. Russia includes no portion of the tropics: the extension of the concept to tropical regions

THE WORLD'S LANDS

has proved more difficult, but the Russians have not hesitated to produce world soil maps.

In the Great Soviet World Atlas there is a World Soil Map prepared by Academician L. I. Prassolov and from this the areas covered by the great soil groups have been calculated by N. N. Rosov. This gives the following results:

TABLE VII

THE GREAT SOIL GROUPS

Soil Types	Million hectares	Million acres	Percentage
Soils of Lowland Territories	*10,831*	*26,753*	*74·7*
Chernozems	394		2·7
Chernozem-like Prairie Soils	214		1·5
Grey Forest Soils	115		0·8
Brown Forest Soils	346		2·4
Red Earths of Subtropics	574		4·0
Alluvial Soils	426		2·9
Chestnut Soils of Dry Steppes	1,020		7·0
Black Soils of Dry Savanna	226		1·6
Cinnamon Soils of Dry Forests	512		3·5
Podzolic Soils	1,375		9·5
Red Earths and Laterites of Tropics	1,389		9·6
Red-Brown Savanna Soils	1,099		7·6
Grey Earths etc. of Desert Steppes	1,408		9·7
Soils of Sandy and Stony Deserts	1,143		7·8
Tundra Soils	590		4·1
Soils of Mountain Territories	*2,433*	*6,009*	*16·8*
Mountain Brown Forest Soils	593		4·1
Mountain Forest Red Earths	63		0·4
Mountain Steppe Soils	269		1·9
Mountain Taiga Podzolic Soils	870		6·0
Mountain Meadow Soils	238		1·6
Mountain Tundra Soils	229		1·6
Soils of Alpine Deserts	171		1·2
Snow and Ice of Antarctica	*1,236*	*3,053*	*8·5*
Total	14,500	35,815	100·0

In his paper read to the Royal Geographical Society in May 1958, Academician I. P. Gerasimov gave a diagram based on the above figures of Rosov from which it is possible to calculate approximately for each type of soil the area actually used for agriculture and the area described as 'of possible use for agriculture (without great amelioration works) based on the existing use of similar soils in the old agricultural regions of the U.S.S.R., China, India and the U.S.A.'

THE WORLD'S LANDS
TABLE VIII

	Million hectares			Unusable at present
	Total	Cultivated	Potential	
Soils of Lowland Territories	10,831	709	2,762	7,360
Chernozems	394	134	142	118
Chernozem-like Prairie Soils	214	50	100	64
Grey Forest Soils	115	32	37	46
Brown Forest Soils	346	87	121	138
Red Earths of Subtropics	574	72	158	344
Alluvial Soils	426	51	162	213
Chestnut Soils of Dry Steppes	1,020	63	345	612
Black Soils of Dry Savanna	226	14	99	113
Cinnamon Soils of Dry Forests	512	26	230	256
Podzolic Soils	1,375	69	412	894
Red Earths and Laterites of Tropics	1,389	56	430	903
Red-Brown Savanna Soils	1,099	24	416	659
Grey Earths etc. of Desert Steppes	1,408	31	110	1,267
Soils of Sandy and Stony Deserts	1,143	—	—	1,143
Tundra Soils	590	—	—	590
Soils of Mountain Territories	2,433	74	165	2,194
Mountain Brown Forest Soils	593	47	42	504
Mountain Forest Red Earths	63	3	6	54
Mountain Steppe Soils	269	11	43	215
Mountain Taiga Podzolic Soils	870	13	74	783
Mountain Meadow Soils	238	—	—	238
Mountain Tundra Soils	229	—	—	229
Soils of Alpine Deserts	171	—	—	171
Snow and Ice of Antarctica	1,236	—	—	1,236
Total	14,500	783	2,927	10,790

The column headed 'cultivated' in the above table is more fully described by Gerasimov as 'areas used for agriculture; under crops, gardens and vineyards (excluding fallows) and is based on the World Agriculture Map by I. G. Makarov in the Great Soviet World Atlas. The total at 783,000,000 hectares or 1,935,000,000 acres would seem to be much too low when compared with FAO statistics which, as quoted above, give a world total of 1,384,000,000 hectares for the same category. The Russian figure is equivalent to slightly less than 0·7 acre per head of world population compared with FAO figure of about 1·2. At the same time the actual plus potential cultivated area at 25·6 per cent of the earth's land surface is one very little less than the *ecumene* postulated by other workers as capable of supporting agriculture.

IV

FOOD FOR ALL

Food for all is the crucial problem of the world today for several reasons. A hungry world is never likely to be a peaceful world. It is not saying too much to suggest that unrest throughout the world most frequently has its root cause in dissatisfaction with that part of the standard of living concerned with food. As Le Gros Clark has put it, a stable civilization will be built only on the foundations of the farm and the kitchen.

We do well to remind ourselves that we consume food for three reasons. A large part of the food we eat 'keeps us going' by providing the body with its heat and energy. It has precisely the same function as fuel performs with our modern machinery. However perfect the machine, it will not function without the right fuel in adequate quantities. Vaguely this idea has been apparent to man for a long time. Our ancestors used to talk about a man's strength failing through lack of food. If for a short time the intake of this fuel is inadequate, the body is able to call upon reserves normally stored in the tissues, but ultimately this stored material is used up and starvation results. For the fuel purposes of food we are concerned particularly with carbohydrates—our daily bread.

In the second place, we consume food for building up the machine itself, that is to say for the development of the body. It is for this purpose that we require particularly the complex substances known as proteins, builders of muscles and other tissues. We have come to realize in recent years the important part played also by those essential substances to which the term vitamin is applied. They are diverse in chemical composition and in function, and they are only required in small quantities; yet they are fundamental in the body's economy, and the body itself cannot manufacture them from simple raw materials. In rather the same way certain chemical elements are necessary in small quantities—calcium for bone, minute quantities of iodine for teeth, small quantities

FOOD FOR ALL

of iron for healthy red blood, and so on, as well as some complex organic substances mentioned below in Chapter VII.

Thirdly, we consume food for what perhaps might be called its psychological effect. In these days the art of gracious living, to which our ancestors were perhaps too much addicted, has been almost forgotten, but probably all of us appreciate that a tastefully served and well-balanced meal, eaten in pleasant surroundings, gives us a greater satisfaction than the same mixture of carbohydrates, proteins and vitamins consumed from a tin mug on the floor. A graphic illustration is afforded by an experiment carried out in a British hospital. Groups of people were served with first-class food—good meat and well-cooked potatoes, but the meat was coloured green and the potatoes magenta and other fierce colours. The majority of the 'guinea pigs' were so affected psychologically that they were ill after the completely innocuous meal.

In the long view a monotonous diet, even if pronounced adequate, will not necessarily maintain the full vigour of either individual or nation, however satisfactory it may be during stress, as in war-time. The widely held view that many people live on an extremely monotonous diet and like it—one thinks of the boiled rice, occasionally flavoured with a little fat pork, and the weak tea of the Chinese—is far from the truth. Given the opportunity and the means, all peoples turn to a varied diet. I have often thought that the finest advice on the subject was that given by the English musical-comedy actress Marie Lloyd in her song of long ago: 'A Little of What You Fancy Does You Good!'

The Daily Diet

The adequacy of our daily bread to maintain the human machine in action—the fuel supply—is measured by the intake of Calories. The nutrition Calorie, which should be written with a capital C, is the kilocalorie of the physicist since it is the amount of heat needed to raise the temperature of 1,000 grams of water by one degree Centigrade—from 15° to 16° C. One gram of carbohydrate absorbed by and oxidized in the body produces 4 Calories and similarly consumption of fats and proteins can be equated with Calorie production in the body.

Nutritionists have shown that there is a minimum consumption of Calories in the ordinary processes of living, that requirement varies naturally with age and period of life, with weight and size of the body, that the requirement rises rapidly with increase in physical activity and

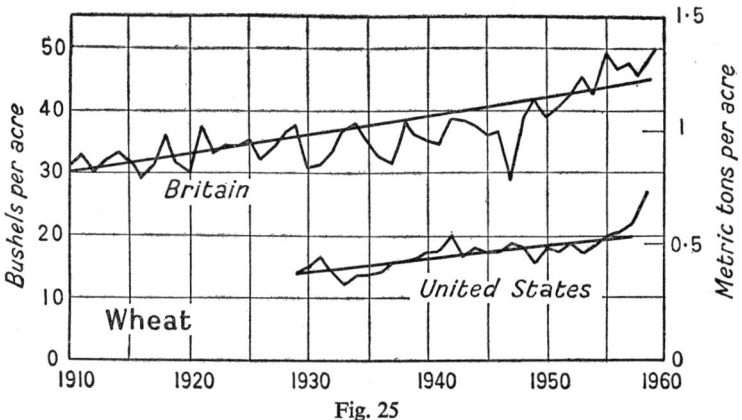

Fig. 25
Wheat yields in Britain and the United States

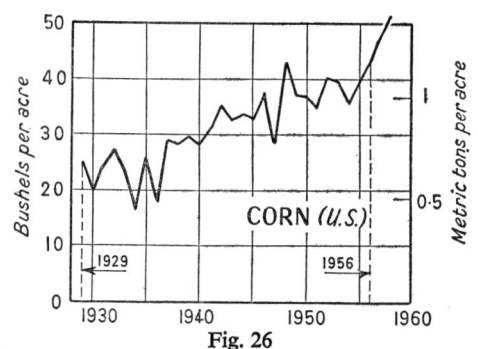

Fig. 26
Corn (maize) yields in the United States. The spectacular rise follows the introduction of hybrid corn

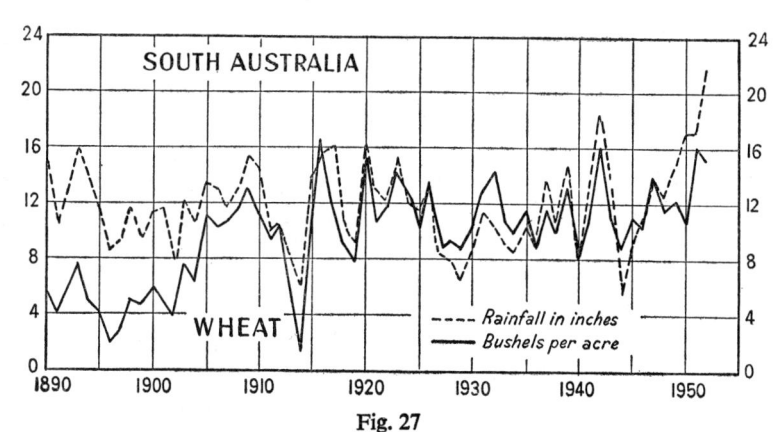

Fig. 27
Wheat yields in South Australia (in part after A. Grenfell Price). Yields are closely dependent on the rainfall of the winter and spring preceding the harvest

in other ways. Some aspects of the food requirements of human beings are considered in Chapter VII, but we may state here the broad position. Where the average—for all ages and all occupations—intake is more than 3,000 Calories a day it is adequate for all purposes and may even be excessive. Where it drops below 2,000 it is below the danger line. It is generally accepted that the desirable caloric intake is somewhere between 2,400 and 2,700. One can gain little guidance from the United States figures, which over a thirty-year period ranged between 3,160 and 3,490 because those figures are obtained by dividing total national Calorie consumption by population, and in fact large amounts of food prepared are not actually consumed.

An adequate fuel intake however is not enough; other essentials enter in. Though there may not be hunger as such, a nutritional problem may exist all the same. The nutritional approach to the problem of feeding human beings in large numbers came to the forefront in World War II. In Britain the Ministry of Food was established as a war-time measure. The Ministry's experts worked out an acceptable diet from nutritional standards and sought to provide it by home production expanded and modified, together with the necessary minimum import. The British farmer was required to concentrate on cereals and potatoes to supply the carbohydrates needed in the supply of human fuel, though with the lowering of the consumption of meat and of the number of animals kept and slaughtered in the country for that purpose the individual's protein intake was reduced. There is no doubt that the whole was well and scientifically worked out and the amazingly good health record of the country during the war is evidence of its success. It is interesting to recall how the third aspect, the palatability of food, caused a minor crisis in the early days of the war. Dietitians will agree that there is little nutritive value in a fried onion compared with other food available, but not only are fried onions able to permeate a home with an odour delectable to some, if odious to others; they also give an almost romantic aroma to the tasteless war-time mixture of bread flavoured with meat scraps put into a skin and called a sausage. And the British, to give zest to their dull, if adequate, war-time diet, demanded onions!

There are many who urge that more attention be given to the protein intake and that in any case carbohydrates derived from such high-protein foods as butcher's meat have a greater effectiveness in their task of maintaining human energy. Despite the health record of Britain and other European countries, there does seem to be some evidence of loss

FOOD FOR ALL

of reserve of stamina or reserve of strength traceable to the lower protein intake during the war years. FAO now publishes estimates of protein intake per head of population in the principal countries. It ranges from less than 50 grammes per day (1949–50) in India, Indo-China and Indonesia to more than 100 in Norway, Argentina, New Zealand, Denmark and Iceland. The United Kingdom, United States and Canada stand together at just under 100 grammes (3·5 oz.).[1] For more than half the world, however, *animal* protein (i.e. meat) is less than 10 grammes (one-third of an ounce) per day.

Estimates of World Food Production

Since the publication of *Our Undeveloped World* in 1953 much more information has become available concerning the total production of food in the world. The information is carefully collected, sifted and analysed before publication by FAO. The detailed tables which the Organization publishes (see Table IX) exclude U.S.S.R., eastern Europe and China. If estimates for these countries are included, world totals are of the following order:

	Million metric tons
Wheat	200–210
Maize	165–170
Oats	70–75
Rice	205
Rye	45
Barley	80–85
Millets	75

This gives a world total output of the major cereals of between 840 and 865 million tons. Of course a proportion of these cereals is fed to animals and so serves only indirectly as human food. We may hazard a guess that the bulk of wheat, rice and millets are used directly as human food, perhaps a quarter of the maize and barley, half the rye and 10 per cent of the oats. This would give about 500,000,000 tons of cereals to feed 2,850,000,000 people. This is 387 lb. a year or a little over 1 lb. of cereal as produced by the farmer per head per day as a world average. Allowing for wastage in milling and preparation, we can say about 15 oz. or 430 grams a day. Since a rough average caloric equivalent of the

[1] FAO *Monthly Bulletin*, February 1952.

FOOD FOR ALL

various grains is 360 per 100 grams, the human race as a whole derives 1,550 Calories a day from the staple cereals.

If we accept 2,500 Calories a day as a reasonable standard intake for health we see at once how low is the standard for the world as a whole. Though in the more advanced peoples there is less and less reliance on bread and cereals generally—witness the diets of the wealthier Americans and north-west Europeans—for three-quarters of mankind the cereals are still the basis of diet. Some actual examples from India are given later, showing how deficiencies are made up.

Turning now to Table IX, showing the growth in world food production since the pre-war years 1934–38, there are some spectacular increases. If the 'index of all farm products' can be relied upon, it suggests that at present food supplies are increasing more rapidly than population—though this world picture is not necessarily true everywhere. FAO does in fact publish tables of caloric intake in the principal countries of the world. Whereas 38 per cent of the people recorded in the pre-war (1934–38) period had less than 2,000 Calories a day, by 1949–50 this percentage had increased to 60 per cent.[1]

Another very interesting conclusion results from a study of the table. It is that, with a world-wide rise in the standard of living, there is a smaller reliance on the staple food grains, and a greater demand for a diversified diet. In the years before the outbreak of World War II it was estimated that the peoples of the United States, Canada, New Zealand, Australia, Britain, Switzerland and Sweden—11 per cent of mankind, with the highest food standards—derived less than 40 per cent of their caloric intake from the staples. Most of the countries of western Europe derived less than 50 per cent from cereals.[2]

As M. K. Bennett, Executive Director of the Food Research Institute of Stanford University, has emphasized on several occasions, a decreasing *per capita* consumption of cereals may indicate an increasing standard of living. The statement applies to most, if not all, of the nations belonging to the commercial Western world. Dr. Bennett postulates that a race of millionaires would not rely on cereals for more than 10 to 20 per cent of caloric intake.[3]

Elsewhere we urge that extensive farming, with huge areas devoted to one crop such as wheat or corn and emphasis on low cost per unit pro-

[1] FAO *Monthly Bulletin*, January 1952.

[2] See the table quoted by F. Le Gros Clark, *Feeding the Human Family* (London, 1947), p. 31.

[3] 'Population and Food Supply: The Current Scare', *Scientific Monthly*, LXVIII (1949), 17–26, with bibliography.

duced, is an obsolescent type of land use. For the conservation of the land itself, it must give place to a balanced type of mixed farming, probably in small units. This seems also to be the lesson to be drawn from studies of changes in human tastes and the trend towards a varied diet.

TABLE IX

Estimated World Production of Major Foodstuffs

Million metric tons

	1934–38	1948–52	1955–56	1956–57	1957–58
Wheat	95·0	113·5	123·4	123·3	122·4
Barley	28·5	36·0	46·4	52·5	49·7
Oats	37·5	42·5	45·7	43·8	40·8
Maize	94·1	119·6	129·8	136·1	137·6
Rice (milled equivalent)	70·2	74·8	87·6	92·1	88·2
Sugar	20·0	26·4	32·0	33·5	35·6
Citrus fruits	11·1	15·1	18·1	17·9	17·3
Apples	11·0	12·6	12·8	14·6	9·0
Bananas	8·1	11·2	12·3	12·7	12·7
Vegetable oils	9·2	11·6	13·4	14·7	14·9
Animal fats	3·01	4·20	4·94	5·26	5·14
Coffee	2·41	2·25	2·86	2·60	2·98
Cocoa	0·74	0·76	0·83	0·91	0·76
Tea	0·47	0·57	0·70	0·70	0·71
Milk	193·6	204·8	229·1	233·8	241·8
Meat	26·9	30·5	37·4	39·0	39·2
Eggs	5·82	7·49	8·83	8·99	9·10
Index of all farm products	85	100	115	118	117
Population index	90 (1935)	100 (1950)	108·7 (1955)	110·4 (1956)	112·2 (1957)

Excluding U.S.S.R., eastern Europe and China

Comparisons and Contrasts between Countries

Since one of our main objects is to discover which of the countries of the world may justifiably be described as under-developed, we need to examine existing production in individual countries. A country may be under-developed either because it has land which could be, but is not, actually productive or because existing production from its farmed lands is below standard, as evidenced by the yield of crops per unit area.

It will be sufficient to illustrate the contrasts between countries by taking a few examples. I have chosen the chief cereals widely used as human food—wheat, rye, corn (maize) and rice, together with one cash crop—sugar cane—so important to many less developed countries. I have endeavoured to get away from that unsatisfactory measure, the bushel, since the weight of a bushel varies from one cereal to another as well as to some extent from one country to another, and have used weight. Since FAO uses metric tons (2,204 lb.) per hectare (2.47 acres) I have given my figures in metric tons both per hectare and per acre, contrasting the pre-war average (1934–38) with the post-war average (1948–52) and the latest year for which details were available at the time of writing.

In each case the general story is the same. There is first the enormous difference in yield between one country and another. This stems from a variety of causes. The physical factor of climate with an adequate and properly distributed supply of moisture, freedom from droughts and extremes of temperature, combined with good soils, puts north-west Europe in the lead, and results in the low yields of Spain and Australia with their constant struggle against the vagaries of climate. Intensity of farming, as contrasted with large scale extensive methods, puts up the already high yields of north-western Europe contrasted with the United States. It is however to be noted that relatively primitive methods—as in Egypt—can give very high yields, especially if combined with heavy use of fertilizer and cultivation skill as in Japan, whereas the tragically low yields in much of India reflect inadequacies in the human factor rather than vagaries of climate.

In the second place there is a marked improvement of yield almost universally—a matter to be discussed in Chapter VII—which is certainly encouraging. It is to be noted that the effects of war-time neglect and devastation have been overcome.

TABLE X
Wheat
Metric Tons

1934–38 per ha	1934–38 per acre		1948–52 per ha	1948–52 per acre	1956 per ha	1956 per acre
3·04	1·23	Denmark	3·65	1·48	4·03	1·63
3·03	1·23	Netherlands	3·65	1·48	3·59	1·45
2·73	1·11	Belgium	3·22	1·30	3·16	1·28
2·31	0·94	United Kingdom	2·72	1·10	3·12	1·26
2·30	0·93	Germany	2·62	1·06	3·02	1·22
2·01	0·81	Egypt	1·84	0·75	2·34	0·95
1·88	0·76	Japan	1·85	0·75	2·09	0·85
1·56	0·63	France	1·83	0·74	2·07	0·84
1·44	0·58	Italy	1·52	0·62	1·78	0·72
1·41	*0·57*	*Europe Average*	*1·48*	*0·60*	*1·58*	*0·64*
1·40	0·57	Hungary	1·38	0·56	1·33	0·54
1·08	0·44	China	0·73	0·30	—	—
1·01	0·41	WORLD AVERAGE	1·05	0·43	1·16	0·47
0·98	0·40	Argentina	1·15	0·47	1·32	0·54
0·96	0·39	Spain	0·87	0·35	0·97	0·39
0·93	0·38	U.S.S.R.	—	—	—	—
0·87	0·35	United States	1·12	0·45	1·35	0·55
0·85	0·34	Pakistan	0·87	0·35	0·74	0·30
0·80	0·32	Australia	1·12	0·45	1·16	0·47
0·71	0·29	Canada	1·28	0·52	1·69	0·68
0·59	0·24	India	0·66	0·27	0·71	0·29

One bushel of wheat = 60 lb. Yield in bushels = metric tons × 36·7.

Most noticeable is the great increase in area yields in Canada, the United States and Argentina.

This table is really most remarkable because it shows that the steady rather than spectacular rise in area yields has been shared by practically every major producer. Yet the countries have retained with little change their relative positions. In 1934–38 Belgium and the Netherlands produced per hectare or per acre four times as much rye as Argentina; in 1956 the proportion was the same. Production in the extensively farmed lands of Canada and the United States is still only a third of that in the intensively farmed countries of north-western Europe.

TABLE XI
Rye
Metric Tons

1934–38			1948–52		1956	
per ha	*per acre*		*per ha*	*per acre*	*per ha*	*per acre*
2·39	0·96	Belgium	2·61	1·04	2·88	1·15
2·27	0·91	Netherlands	2·59	1·04	2·88	1·15
1·93	0·77	Sweden	2·02	0·81	2·17	0·87
1·79	0·72	Germany	2·21	0·88	2·33	0·93
1·78	0·71	Denmark	2·37	0·95	2·67	1·07
1·60	0·64	Czechoslovakia	1·75	0·70	2·04	0·82
1·42	*0·57*	*Europe Average*	*1·47*	*0·69*	*1·58*	*0·63*
1·34	0·54	Italy	1·27	0·51	1·45	0·58
1·31	0·52	WORLD AVERAGE	1·34	0·54	1·43	0·57
1·28	0·51	Poland	1·26	0·50	1·32	0·54
1·16	0·46	France	1·15	0·46	1·27	0·51
1·11	0·44	Hungary	1·23	0·49	1·12	0·45
—	—	Turkey	1·01	0·40	0·88	0·35
0·99	0·40	U.S.S.R.	—	—	—	—
0·93	0·37	Spain	0·77	0·31	0·84	0·34
0·77	0·31	United States	0·76	0·30	0·82	0·33
0·61	0·24	Canada	0·83	0·33	0·99	0·40
0·58	0·23	Argentina	0·73	0·29	0·72	0·29

One bushel of rye = 60 lb. Yield in bushels = metric tons × 36·7

TABLE XII
Corn (Maize)
Metric Tons

1934–38			1948–52		1956	
per ha	per acre		per ha	per acre	per ha	per acre
2·84	1·14	Germany	2·19	0·88	2·67	1·07
2·55	1·02	Austria	2·05	0·82	2·81	1·12
2·53	1·01	Canada	3·20	1·28	3·43	1·37
2·49	1·00	Egypt	2·09	0·84	2·14	0·86
2·05	0·82	Italy	1·84	0·74	2·71	1·08
1.99	0·80	Hungary	1·78	0·71	1·76	0·70
1·81	0·72	Argentina	1·48	0·59	1·38	0·55
1·58	0·63	France	1·38	0·55	2·66	1·08
1·51	0·60	United States	2·45	0·98	2·87	1·15
1·48	*0·59*	*Europe Average*	*1·27*	*0·51*	*1·55*	*0·62*
1·39	0·56	Brazil	1·24	0·50	1·27	0·51
1·38	0·55	China	—	—	—	—
1·34	0·54	WORLD AVERAGE	1·58	0·63	1·72	0·69
—	—	Yugoslavia	1·38	0·55	1·31	0·52
1·13	0·45	Bulgaria	1·06	0·42	1·33	0·53
1·11	0·44	Pakistan	0·98	0·39	1·08	0·43
1·07	0·43	U.S.S.R.	—	—	—	—
1·04	0·42	Roumania	0·81	0·32	1·10	0·44
0·97	0·39	Java	0·68	0·26	0·84	0·32
0·81	*0·32*	*Africa Average*	*0·83*	*0·33*	*0·96*	*0·38*
0·74	0·30	India	0·65	0·26	0·82	0·33
0·60	0·24	South Africa	0·90	0·36	0·11	0·44
0·56	0·22	Mexico	0·75	0·30	0·80	0·32
—	—	Philippines	0·72	0·29	0·50	0·20

One bushel of maize = 60 lb. Yield in bushels = metric tons × 36·7.

In contrast to the table for wheat and rye and some other cereals, the changes shown above are spectacular, almost magical, with the introduction of hybrid corn in the United States and those countries which have followed the American lead.

TABLE XIII
Paddy (Rice)
Metric Tons

1934–38 per ha	1934–38 per acre		1948–52 per ha	1948–52 per acre	1956 per ha	1956 per acre
6·23	2·52	Spain	4·66	1·89	5·81	2·35
5·28	2·14	Italy	4·87	1·97	4·69	1·90
4·78	1·93	Australia	4·86	1·97	5·29	2·14
3·63	1·47	Japan	4·00	1·62	4·22	1·71
3·49	1·41	Egypt	3·79	1·53	5·43	2·20
2·53	1·02	China	2·16	0·87	—	—
2·48	1·00	British Guiana	2·23	0·90	2·42	0·98
2·47	1·00	United States	2·56	1·04	3·53	1·43
2·36	0·96	Korea	2·78	1·13	2·29	0·93
1·76	0·71	WORLD AVERAGE	1·59	0·64	1·86	0·75
1·52	0·62	Java	1·57	0·64	1·67	0·68
1·48	0·60	Pakistan	1·38	0·56	1·51	0·61
1·43	0·58	Brazil	1·57	0·64	1·65	0·67
1·43	0·58	Thailand	1·31	0·53	1·43	0·58
1·41	0·57	Burma	1·41	0·57	1·60	0·65
1·31	0·53	India	1·11	0·45	1·36	0·55
1·23	0·50	Madagascar	1·35	0·55	1·31	0·53
1·09	0·44	Philippines	1·19	0·48	1·21	0·49

One bushel of paddy = 45 lb. Yield in bushels = metric tons × 49.
Rice production is characterized by an enormous range in yield which is intensified by the possibility of double and treble cropping in some countries.

TABLE XIV
Sugar Cane
Metric Tons

1934–38			1948–52		1956	
per ha	*per acre*		*per ha*	*per acre*	*per ha*	*per acre*
151·2	60·4	Hawaii	177·4	71·0	209·1	83·6
130·2	52·0	Java (plantation)	57·5	23·0	147·8	59·1
104·4	40·9	Peru	133·0	53·2	—	—
81·9	32·7	Egypt	72·8	29·1	124·2	49·7
63·4	25·3	Jamaica	58·4	23·4	60·1	24·0
59·8	23·9	Puerto Rico	65·8	26·3	67·3	26·9
54·0	21·6	Fiji	50·4	20·2	43·5	17·4
51·9	20·7	Australia	59·7	23·9	58·5	23·4
46·6	18·6	Mexico	51·3	20·5	—	—
44·4	17·3	United States	45·7	18·3	58·0	23·2
42·3	16·8	Mauritius	58·4	23·4	62·3	24·9
41·1	16·4	Trinidad	60·4	24·2	97·5	39·0
37·8	15·1	Cuba	38·3	15·3	—	—
37·7	15·0	Brazil	38·7	15·5	38·1	15·2
35·9	14·3	WORLD AVERAGE	?		?	
35·0	14·0	Philippines	45·0	18·0	48·1	19·2
32·0	12·8	Argentina	33·2	13·3	30·7	12·2
25·8	10·3	South Africa	57·0	22·8	71·2	28·5
?	?	India	32·1	12·8	32·9	13·2

Quite apart from the enormous range in yield of cane—the best nearly seven times the poorest—it should be noted that there is a great variation in the yield of sugar per ton of cane—with a marked general improvement. In countries with well-equipped mills a ton of sugar is made from 7½ to 8½ tons of cane; in countries where there is much production on a small scale, like India, it requires over 12 tons of cane.

FOOD FOR ALL

Feeding the Multitude

The problem of today is not so much the feeding of the multitude as the feeding of the increasing multitude. If, as we have seen, it takes the produce on a world average of rather over one acre of cultivated land to feed one person, it may be argued that, to feed a net increase of 54,000,000 persons a year, a net new acreage of 54,000,000 must be brought into cultivation every year. When one remembers that the total acreage of improved farm land in England and Wales is only a little over 24,000,000 and in Great Britain as a whole only 28,500,000, the enormity of the task is at once apparent. Actually the position viewed on a simple areal basis is far worse than these figures suggest because of the huge acreage being lost to cultivation annually through soil erosion.[1] There are some who would have us believe that the loss in this way more than balances the intake through reclamation. But there is another way of meeting the problem. If the world population is increasing at the net rate of 1·8 per cent per annum, it is only necessary to increase net production of food from the existing cultivated acreage by the same percentage of 1·8 per cent to maintain the present level of food supply to the individual. Not in the case of any staple food does the world level of yield begin to approach the yield in the better farmed lands (see Tables X–XIV)—indeed it is usually less than half, whilst the yield in the less efficient countries is often only a quarter or a fifth of that in their well-farmed neighbours.

Thus a modest increase in acreage, together with a modest increase in yield can keep the world at its present level of nutrition for at least a good many years to come. The indications are that, again viewing the world as a whole, food production is rather more than keeping pace with population (Table IX).

But there are countries where the struggle to do this is indeed severe. We may mention Japan, discussed in some detail on page 113. In India where the population increase is of the order of 8,000,000 persons a year, cultivated acreage, even if the Plans are completely fulfilled, do not allow for reclamation of land at the rate of 22,000 acres a day, or an acre every four seconds. In Pakistan, where vast works are in progress, two acres a minute reclaimed would scarcely keep pace with population.

---

[1] It has been claimed that in the United States between 40 and 50 per cent of the original fertility of the land has been lost since the First World War by water and wind erosion, over-cropping and over-grazing.

FOOD FOR ALL

It so happens that in these countries the crop yields are very low, and the agricultural revolution has scarcely begun. It does not sound such a formidable task to increase the yield of rice from, say, 28 bushels an acre to 30 bushels—which is over 7 per cent—more especially when one remembers that Egypt already produces over 100 bushels an acre.

Pessimism turns to optimism when one contemplates what recent developments in agriculture have actually been accomplished elsewhere.

V

THE NEW AGRICULTURAL REVOLUTION

In the seventeenth and eighteenth centuries changes in farming practice in western Europe, which collectively may be called the Agricultural Revolution, spread but slowly within given countries or from one country to another. Similarly the change from hand machine to power machine and from home workshop to factory which collectively may be called the Industrial Revolution took place in different countries at different times. Two centuries old in western Europe, it is just taking place in many parts of the world. With the new Agricultural Revolution there is similarly a great range in intensity of incidence but with this difference. International agencies now exist able and ready to spread to any country willing to learn the latest results of scientific work. Sometimes methods successful in one part of the world or under one set of circumstances are not directly applicable in others. This is abundantly true when experience in mid-latitudes is applied without due caution in the tropics. The cultivator often knows instinctively the dangers and so hesitates to accept immediately the advice of strangers, however expert. Yet he only succeeds in earning for himself the reputation of being stubborn or, at best, conservative.

If we start by examining what the new Agricultural Revolution means in Britain it must therefore be with the caution that elsewhere the whole picture may be, or indeed is, very different.

In Britain the effects of the revolution to date—it is definitely still in full swing—may be summarized by saying that output has been increased by more than 60 per cent in the twenty-five years covering the period from the mid-thirties to 1958 from the same or a slightly smaller area of land and with a much decreased labour force. This has been achieved in the main by a combination of mechanization and chemicalization or the collaboration of the engineer and chemist with the plant and animal geneticist.

Mechanization was well under way in the inter-war years and

THE NEW AGRICULTURAL REVOLUTION

gathered great momentum during the war at the expense of the horse. If the tractor had to be fed—with imported fuel—so did the horse and often too with imported feeding stuffs and certainly with the produce of land which could be used for the production of human food. Compared with the horse, the tractor is both strong and fast. The tractor-plough can deal effectively with heavy land which once needed three or four horses to pull a single-furrow plough. The saving of time is not the only advantage of speed. Some land can only be ploughed when it is neither too wet nor too dry—the tractor-drawn plough can deal with this on just the few days which may be suitable. The first trend in mechanization was mainly the substitution of the tractor for the horse. The plough, the harrow, the roller, the reaper remained. Judged by number of implements per acre of cultivated land, Britain became the most highly mechanized country in the world. The question naturally arose whether the range of implements was fully or effectively used, or was the whole a form of uneconomic mechanization? In the later war years there had been state-controlled pools of machinery in each county; it was in the post-war years that this question arose. The trend recently has been towards an increasing complexity of farm machinery. The combine-harvester of the wide open prairies was an early development of this trend. It was adapted on a smaller scale for British use, but machines like the rotary tiller—combining functions of plough, disc and harrow—are now designed also to carry out in one operation what were formerly separate tasks and again to take advantage of weather conditions during brief spells when they may be favourable. Some modern farm machines are indeed almost terrifying in their complexity: the farm worker must be a first-class mechanic. When things go really wrong it is no longer a job for the village blacksmith turned garage proprietor, but for a properly equipped service station most likely located in the county town or market centre of comparable status. If the farm relies on the urban factory for the supply of its modern equipment, it continues to do so for its maintenance. In the earlier years of the present century ploughing was often done under contract by owners of steam traction-engines adapted for the purpose. Contractors still exist who carry out ploughing but the tractor has tended to make the farmer more independent. Just as the internal combustion engine has replaced the steam-engine in the fields, in the farmstead electricity has largely replaced all other forms of motive power. For long the electricity supply authorities talked of the impossibility of rural electrification because of the cost of installation. They did not realize that whereas the

THE NEW AGRICULTURAL REVOLUTION

TABLE XV
MECHANIZATION OF FARMING IN BRITAIN

	1939	May 1942	Jan. 1948	Jan. 1956
Tractors:				
Total	52,000	116,830	261,180	477,700
Tracklayers		5,600	15,200	17,970
3- and 4-wheeled		104,780	220,350	394,450
Market garden types		6,450	28,120	65,280
Mouldboard ploughs:				
Total		465,630	462,940	
Horsedrawn		353,180	218,380	
Tractor drawn		112,450	244,560	340,690
Disc harrows		33,840	76,060	100,200
Cultivators		161,690	256,670	c500,000
Farmyard manure spreaders		—	—	65,390
Mowing machines		220,420	231,520	222,220
Pick-up balers		—	1,980	39,830
Combine harvesters	150	1,000	5,220	32,890
Grain and grass driers		—	1,550	9,380
Milking machines		29,510	58,210	c110,000
Working horses	668,000	585,000	457,000	124,000

The total number of 'holdings'—many 'part-time' or 'hobby-farms' and some as small as one acre—is about 363,000 in England and Wales and 74,000 in Scotland—a total of about 437,000.

The total number of *full-time* farms or farmers in England and Wales is about 216,000 (1941 Farm Survey) to which should be added about 50,000 for Scotland, say 266,000 in all.

The above table suggests that by 1948 the great majority of full-time farmers owned a tractor, a tractor-drawn plough, a cultivator and a mowing machine or binder. By 1956 most full-time farmers obviously had more than one tractor. As the number of working horses continued to drop to 105,000 on 1st January 1957, and lower still in succeeding years, only about one full-time farmer in three still had a horse in 1958.

townsman wants a few lights and perhaps an electric cooking stove and a portable fire, the farmer immediately thinks in terms of electric milking, chaff cutting, threshing, probably pumping and wood-cutting and a dozen other applications of electric power once it is available. The farmer is today a more profitable customer than the townsman. Two other aspects of mechanization must be mentioned. It is fast becoming rare to find a full-time farmer without his own car; collection of milk by motor lorry is universal and so is transport of animals to market. Of course the farmer is on the phone; the fact that his cowman is also, obviates the vital need of the past for the cowman to be on a tied cottage on the farm.

TABLE XVI

Chemicalization of Farming in Britain
(Tons)

	1946–47	1947–48	1957–58
Nitrogenous fertilizers:			
N_2 content: deliveries to farms	163,600	186,000	309,800
Phosphatic fertilizers:			
P_2O_5 content: deliveries	356,900	395,600	366,000
Superphosphate:			
Deliveries	197,000	225,000	151,200
Ground Basic Slag:			
Deliveries	70,200	82,300	103,200
Ground Phosphate			
Deliveries	41,000	43,600	16,800
Other phosphatic fertilizers:			
Deliveries	48,700	44,500	94,800
Potash:			
K_2O content: deliveries			348,120
Compound fertilizers:[1]			
Deliveries	1,291,000	1,565,700	2,390,400
Phosphate rock:[2]			
Deliveries	831,400	1,005,800	1,250,400

[1] Total weight of product. The N_2–P_2O_5 and K_2O content are included under the appropriate headings above.
[2] Including some for industrial purposes.

Table kindly supplied by Mr. F. H. Braybrook of Petrochemicals Limited.

Chemicalization is newer. The gradual replacement of farmyard manure by dressings of lime, Chilean nitrate, slag and superphosphates has gathered pace. The big manufacturers and suppliers prepare balanced fertilizers to suit specific soil and climatic conditions and specified crops, and dressings can be on a scale scarcely contemplated a few years ago. Table XVI covering only the short period of eleven years shows the chemicalization of British farms comparable with the table of mechanization. Sir William Ogg, quoting estimates by G. W. Cooke, notes the exhausting effects on nutrients in the soil resulting from modern farming methods.

Loss of plant nutrients in lb. per acre

	N	P	K
Old four-course feeding rotation	57	18	7
Modern cash-cropping rotation	390	128	435

But what does this prove? The agricultural chemist naturally uses it to demonstrate the enormous demand of modern farming for fertilizers. Certainly the yield of crops has increased considerably but not in anything like the same proportion as the increase in amounts of fertilizers required. There are those who would argue therefore that the use of chemical fertilizers has almost entirely destroyed the 'natural' fertility of the soil. They argue that these fantastic quantities of expensive artificials are needed to make good the loss of organic manures formerly manufactured naturally by the denizens of the soil itself (see below, page 91).

The realization that there are widespread deficiency diseases in plants which can be corrected by the application of quantities, often minute, of trace elements is another aspect of chemicalization. So too is the control of pests and diseases by innumerable sprays and powders. As with

TABLE XVII

World Consumption of Fertilizers

(*Metric Tons*)

	1952–53	1956–57
Nitrogen	4,883,000	6,600,000
Phosphate	6,092,000	7,324,000
Potash	4,883,000	6,172,000

Approximately half is used in Europe, rather over a quarter in North America.

'The average rate of fertilizer consumption per thousand hectares of agricultural land is more than seven times higher for the developed countries than it is for the under-developed.' State of Agriculture. FAO, 1958, pp. 70–71.)

human beings, so many of the old killing diseases of cattle and sheep are now little to be feared. Tuberculosis is on the way to being exterminated and so is contagious abortion, but in their place the disorders of the digestive and nervous systems now so common among human beings are paralleled amongst farm animals, with the prevalence of the so-called metabolic diseases. The cowman must now be something of a vet, with a needle and vaccine, or with some of the new drugs such as sulphonamides, always to hand: the day may not be far distant when he will need to be an animal psycho-analyst as well. Back in the fields growth is further controlled by a wide range of weed killers, many highly selective as well as very potent. Here new dangers appear: the wrong weed killer may do immense damage; even an unnoticed breeze may waft the killer-chemical on to the wrong crops hundreds of yards

THE NEW AGRICULTURAL REVOLUTION

away. Another development, at present of limited application, is of soil 'conditioners' such as krilium, which may alter the physical structure of a soil—for example converting a stiff clay into the equivalent of an easily workable loam. At present high cost is against their widespread use. The counteracting of salt (sodium chloride) in reclaimed salt marshes or land damaged by sea-water flooding by applications of gypsum (calcium sulphate) may be quoted as another example of soil conditioning by chemicals.

The plant geneticist has many parts to play. Increased yield of cereals has been due both to the development of high yielding strains and to the exploitation of hybrid vigour. There is the constant effort to evolve disease-resistant varieties; to find those which can flout some of the old limitations, such as length of the growing season or accumulated temperatures above 42° F. or length of daylight. Among the noteworthy achievements in British agriculture are the development of leafy strains of grasses, such as Italian rye grass, which anticipate the spring, and give good crops (for grazing or grass silage) by May or earlier.

There are many new aspects of animal husbandry which have gone far beyond selective breeding to develop desirable traits and eliminate bad. It is now well known that animals are particularly influenced by daylight. By artificially lengthening the hours of daylight hens can be induced to lay earlier in the year and produce larger eggs. The reproductive cycle of both sheep and cattle can be varied by artificially lengthening or shortening the days. Of other climatic factors susceptible of partial control, the supply of moisture is obviously one. Irrigation in arid lands we discuss elsewhere but it has come to be realized that even in a land of abundant moisture such as Britain, control of available water is important. In most parts of the country drainage and the prevention of acid conditions in the soil are vital, but in spring and summer careful studies of evaporation and evapotranspiration have shown the usual occurrence of moisture-deficiency periods. It is now accepted that in south-eastern England moisture deficiency may occur, in at least one month, in nine seasons out of ten. The new systems of sprinkler irrigation give remarkable increases in yield of certain vegetables.

A modern development which has not yet hit the British farmer with full force is that of quick freezing or deep freezing. Most meats, fish, fruit and vegetables with a minimal suitable preparation put quickly into a freezing chamber at a temperature of about 15° F. soon freeze solid and keep indefinitely, preserving their full flavour. Some British farms are acquiring such a freezer, some European countries, e.g.

THE NEW AGRICULTURAL REVOLUTION

Austria, have a 'locker club' as a regular village feature where the freezers are let out to farmers who bring in their produce for freezing and storage. The system, apart from the present high initial cost of the freezer, is ideal for the large garden which can then permit the owner to live on his own produce throughout the year.[1] This is again a boon resulting from an electric supply. Surprising as it may seem the deep freeze has opened up a new development. It is found that animal semen can be kept for long periods and retain its full quality: by artificial insemination a chosen bull can sire calves years after it has been killed, and this is now common practice; moreover the semen can be used diluted, permitting a far greater number of services from a selected bull. The use of artificial insemination itself is one of the most amazing features of the new agricultural revolution. Though demonstrated as practicable by Sir John Hammond at Cambridge many years before, it was the urgency of war-time conditions during the Second World War which vanquished both the prejudice of farmers and the vested interests of pedigree breeders; A.I. centres were set up during the war; within fifteen years the Milk Marketing Board, which runs most of the centres, was celebrating in January 1959 the completion of the first 10 million inseminations, and the fact that half the dairy cattle in Britain had been bred artificially. The average increase in milk yields per cow of 25 per cent over the same period is obviously closely connected with the use of carefully selected semen. Now attention is being turned to similar methods for increasing beef quality, to the coupling of A.I. and hormone injections to produce twins. It is small wonder that the modern farmer, even if he owns a bull, is apt to tell his cowman: don't use the bull, use the telephone.

Considering still the British position, what is the effect of this revolution on farm layout and the landscape? It is less than might be expected. The changes in technique affect the individual farm: there has been little tendency towards larger units than the 100-acre average. The farmhouse is brighter with electricity; the kitchen and the dairy are modernized; substantial old buildings have been adapted, perhaps added to. There is a trend towards standardization and interchangeable units in farm buildings, but here also a rapid evolution of thought is at work. 'Deep

---

[1] In my own case I have found ideal results with fresh-caught mackerel, spring chicken as fryers, capons, ducks, a range of fruit but especially raspberries, black, red and white currants, blackberries, strawberries (less successful), apple puree and especially apple juice, a wide range of vegetables but especially peas, broad beans, runner beans, mushrooms and asparagus. Each can be put down when in perfect condition; there is never a glut which cannot be used.

THE NEW AGRICULTURAL REVOLUTION
TABLE XVIII
The Increase in Farming Efficiency in Great Britain

Per 100 acres of improved land (crops and grass)

	Workers	Arable %	Wheat acres	Total cattle	Milch cows	Sheep	Work horses
1874	4·7	58	11·6	19·6	—	97	4·2
1939	2·2	40	5·6	28·0	9·0	85	2·6
1945	2·9[a]	61	11·2[b]	31·0	9·4	65	—
1947[c]	3·3[d]	60	7·0	30·8	9·3	54	1·7
1951[c]	2·6	58	6·9	33·6	9·8	64	—
1957[c]	2·1	56	6·8	35·1	10·7	80	0·4

Acres and animals per worker[a]

	Crops and grass	Arable	Wheat	Total cattle	Milch cows	Sheep	Horses
1874	21·3	12·3	2·5	4·2	—	20·7	0·9
1939	44·5	18·1	2·4	12·5	4·0	37·8	1·2
1945	35·0	21·6	4·1[b]	10·9	3·3	22·7	—
1951	38·3	22·2	2·6	12·9	3·7	24·6	—
1957	48·1	27·2	3·3	16·9	5·2	38·4	0·2

a. Workers include farmers and labourers and in 1945 about 80,000 members of the Women's Land Army and also prisoners of war.
b. 1943.
c. United Kingdom.
d. Including part-time and self-employed.

litter' for poultry is being paralleled by cowsheds with floors of strong wood slats through which manure drops and where there is no need for straw. There has been a rationalization of field boundaries and shapes, some hedges and hedgerow trees have gone; the others are well kept and there is evidence of ditching and draining. There is more arable and less permanent grass than before the Second World War and the farmer is no longer tied to any definite system of rotation. Some crops, notably marrow-stem kale, are more in evidence, whilst the traditional roots, swedes and mangolds, are less so. There is a tendency to specialize and cut out time-consuming sidelines. The typical mixed English farm has

THE NEW AGRICULTURAL REVOLUTION

been described in the past as a mixture of zoo and botanic garden: this is no longer true.

Generally speaking the old uneducated farm worker has gone. His successor is a specialist, but one with a remarkably wide knowledge. Because of the decreased labour force and the concentration of services in neighbouring towns—so easily reached by the farmer in his car—village life is difficult to maintain. At first the country bus services destroyed the old isolation of the village: now the services are threatened by the increase in private car ownership.

This sketch of the new agricultural revolution to date has been referred to British conditions. How far is it applicable to other countries? In certain aspects it is already almost world wide, but not in all. In the intensively farmed countries of north-western Europe it is happening in an intensified form, but in the Mediterranean countries of southern Europe there are obstacles scarcely known in Britain. One widespread difficulty is the fragmentation and small size of holdings so that some consolidation into 'viable' or 'economic' holdings is a first need. Great progress has been made in many countries in this work of consolidation —the Irish Republic, France and Italy for example. Even if this is achieved elsewhere the new holdings as planned would only be classed as smallholdings in Britain. The landlord and tenant system which, on the whole, works so well in Britain, in many countries is a symbol of an outmoded feudalism, and the aim is owner-occupation.

Most countries are experiencing some degree of mechanization but modified by, first, availability of capital and, second, the cost of labour, so much lower than in Britain. Most countries too are experiencing at least the beginnings of chemicalization—witness the production of ammonium sulphate at Sindhri in the Damodar Valley of India. The most obvious way in which countries can share some of the benefits of the new agriculture is in the adoption of higher-yielding varieties including hybrids. Here obstacles may be availability of seed and cost but local prejudice is a considerable factor. It is in this field, as with improved breeds of animals, that indigenous research stations and international agencies exercise their greatest influence. The remarkable work of Italian experts working at Borgo a Mozzano in Tuscany under Shell Italiana should be noted.

Certain implications of the new agricultural revolution are at present far from being clearly understood. From being a simple, almost primitive, way of life, farming is becoming a highly organized complex business enterprise. The question arises: what proportion of a country's

THE NEW AGRICULTURAL REVOLUTION

population should properly be engaged in this business? We attempt an interim answer to this question in Chapter VII.

What are the great changes most likely ahead? On land, the extravagant production of animal protein may well be by-passed. Many countries with a dense population—Japan, India and Egypt are examples—are paying much attention to fish culture in fresh water, but the cultivation of the sea has scarcely yet begun. With fishing we are scarcely out of the Stone Age hunting era; with marine-plant culture almost the only significant start is the seaweed culture of the Japanese. The possibilities ahead are stupendous. Mankind will not starve—yet.

VI

THE PEDOLOGICAL PARADOX

In his fascinating book, *The World of the Soil*, published in 1957, the veteran soil scientist Sir John Russell brings vividly to our imagination the concept of that thin layer between rock and air as a complete world of its own. In a physical complex partly of mineral particles, partly of organic matter, a structure is developed which the farmer knows well when he speaks of his land being in good heart and his seed-bed in good tilth. The gardener rubs his well-matured soil through his fingers and notes its satisfactory crumb structure. A century ago Charles Darwin recorded meticulously the part played by earthworms in building up the better soils: he was not to know the myriad organisms, many ultra-microscopic and innumerable in their billions, which throng the pore spaces and the channels his visible denizens left. Our picture of this soil world is still very far from complete: we know it has a climate of its own quite different from that of the atmosphere above; we know it has a hydrology of its own and water behaves quite differently from what it may do on the surface above. Water moves almost as often uphill as it does downhill, and plays many roles. A delicate balance is maintained between the minute animals and plants: they are very susceptible to small changes in the environment; they can only carry out their vital tasks, such as decomposing vegetable debris, when conditions are favourable.

Into this soil world there come intruders from the outside in the form of plant roots. Intruders they may be, but in general it is the function of the soil inhabitants to prepare and convey nutrients to the root hairs, circulating soil water providing those same root hairs with vital moisture, the soil structure giving freedom to root development.

Where then is the paradox? Man is not directly concerned with the soil populations themselves, but only in so far as they affect the life of the plants he chooses to grow for his own needs and which find their sustenance in the soil and there develop their roots. He can treat

THE PEDOLOGICAL PARADOX

the soil in two different and sometimes mutually opposing ways.

One way is to build up the soil by encouraging the wide range of soil organisms to multiply and carry out their varied functions. To choose a few examples at random, the conversion of plant remains into humus is the work mainly of certain groups of bacteria: the bacteria will differ according to whether air is freely present (aerobic bacteria) or absent (anaerobic). At the same time attention to drainage and aeration will provide conditions for the development of soil structure suitable for root development. There is no doubt that the natural development of soil is greatly aided by the use of natural manures—themselves mixtures of organic compounds already partly prepared as plant nutrients. Some of those who stress the need for the natural development of soils go so far as to eschew 'chemical' fertilizers; they claim further superior nutrient status as human food of crops grown on 'natural' soils. For long, indeed for centuries, the conservation of good 'natural' soils has been almost synonymous with good husbandry. The phrase 'good husbandry' is one of those delightful survivals of phraseology from a past era which finds a place even in such august surroundings as an Act of Parliament (Agriculture Act, 1947). It has the advantage that each reader knows, or thinks he knows, broadly what it means, but it is incapable of precise definition. It is in the tradition of 'fair-play', 'cricket' or in modern terminology U and non-U. We scarcely get further by saying that a farmer practising good husbandry will leave his land in 'better heart' than he finds it. We then get round to saying that land is in good heart when it has been subject to the practice of good husbandry.

The other way to secure heavy crops of economic plants is to ascertain their special needs and feed the nutrients to them as required. In general terms this is the basis of most modern systems of intensive farming and, as described elsewhere, has been called the chemicalization of agriculture. Whatever the effect on the crop plants, the effect on the soil population and flora is often, at least so we may surmise, disastrous. But does this matter? The soil becomes simply a mixture of inorganic mineral particles through which roots can ramify, and so support the plant. In its extreme form the 'soil' can be simply a sterilized mixture of mineral grains—as it is in some forms of glasshouse cultivation of tomatoes—and the system of farming becomes hydroponics.

The tables given in Chapter V together with the graphs and the recorded changes in Britain over the past twenty-five years leave no doubt as to the progress made in increasing crop yields. Nearly every-

THE PEDOLOGICAL PARADOX

where this is the result, at least in the main, of greater use of chemical fertilizers. At the same time it has been made abundantly clear in this book that the right solution for land use problems in one country is not necessarily the right solution in another. This certainly applies to soil management. Whilst therefore the case for chemicalization seems proved on grounds of improved yields, there are other factors. Is there or is there not any effect on those very intangible but real qualities, the 'taste' of food, and on its nutritive value? Secondly, if the structure of soil so largely dependent on organic material is broken down, will not soil erosion become increasingly dangerous? But if mineral particles can be retained in the necessary proportion is there any need to conserve so-called good agricultural soils? Further, if chemical soil 'conditioners' can be developed, will not costly conservation services be rendered obsolete? Obviously the way ahead is far from clear at the moment, and it is worth while to study some of the implications.

Soil Surveys

In the first place what are the purposes and importance of a soil survey? Some countries are spending millions of pounds on soil surveys; other countries consider them either of little value or entirely unnecessary. There is far from general agreement on aims and methods of survey and certainly too on soil classification. Although there is a Soil Survey Board in Great Britain, until 1959 years of effort failed to get the Directors of the Surveys of Scotland and of England and Wales to agree on a common classification. If left undisturbed by man, most soils develop a succession of layers forming the profile. It is now generally accepted that the character of the profile should form the basis of classification. But the action of the farmer in ploughing is to mix thoroughly together the top 10 or 12 inches of soil and to destroy the profile. It is not difficult to see why some soil scientists claim that only non-agricultural soils can be described and mapped and that soils should always be studied *qua* soils, and not in regard to agricultural or other utilization. But if this is the case, what is the purpose of the survey? In their pioneer work on the *Agriculture and Soils of Kent, Surrey and Sussex* Sir A. Daniel Hall and Sir E. John Russell first mixed the upper layers of their soil samples—as would happen in cultivation—before subjecting them to mechanical and chemical analyses. On the same principle certain areas in Britain in the past were mapped by the Geological Survey with a

THE PEDOLOGICAL PARADOX

classification according to texture—sands, loams, silts and clays. This is essentially the same point of view as that adopted by the county reporters who prepared descriptions and maps of the soil regions in each of the counties of Britain for the newly created Board of Agriculture and Internal Improvement as long ago as 1793–94. It is almost true to say that these remain the only soil maps of Britain over large areas 150 years later. The development of British soil studies in the interim has been governed by two factors. First, the whole of Britain lies essentially in one major climatic region (see Chapter III and Figs. 23 and 24), one of rainfall well distributed throughout the year and small temperature ranges. Though there is a wide difference in total amount of rainfall, the soils have all been developed under a single climatic régime. But the terrain and the base rocks are extremely varied: soils are closely related to the underlying geological structure. They were long described on the basis of the rocks from which they were derived and this is still the fundamental idea of the 'associations' distinguished by the Scottish Soil Survey. Where the modern English and Welsh surveyors have broken away from this it is to isolate and describe the distinctive 'soil series' and then to combine related soil series into larger groups.

The Russian approach, developed originally by Glinka, is fundamentally different. Over the vast monotonous plains of the Soviet Union, largely drift covered, the underlying geological deposits may show little change: not so the climatic differences from north to south or east to west. Consequently great soil groups, coincident broadly with climatic types, can be distinguished and the idea of 'major soil groups' has been extended to cover the world. Russians have been to the fore in this work: their interpretation of the world is well shown by the soil maps in the Great Soviet World Atlas. There is a strong tendency to link land management and agricultural production to major soil groups, and the summary of the position in 1957 (page 64 above) is quoted from Gerasimov.

Generally speaking, the Americans have married the two approaches. Despite the vast size of the country, large areas in many States have been mapped on the 1-inch to the mile or equivalent scales; immense numbers of soil series have been named and described and their correlation is already a huge task. At the same time the broad soil groups have been delineated and mapped and the work carried to other parts of the world. Though there is fairly general agreement on the world groups in mid-latitudes, it is interesting to see the uncertainty which still exists where tropical soils are concerned. We may take the pioneer study of the continent of Africa by C. F. Marbut in 1923, the sweeping re-approach and new nomenclature of C. E. Kellogg and compare these with the Russian generalizations of Z. J. Shokalskaia.

We return to the practical value of soil surveys. It is possible to lay down for each major soil group broad principles of management and use. Can they, in fact, be equated with 'land capability' classes? On a small scale can the management, land use and suitable crops be laid down even for a single soil series? Some will answer that this is the only scientific approach and that the soil survey is the essential basis for land planning. There can be little doubt that an objective soil survey is a very valuable scientific weapon in approaching the problem of correct land use, but it is far from being the *only* basis of operations.

In making this assertion we have in mind the trend of events in the new agricultural revolution. Experience shows that mechanization is limited by the type of terrain—that change and progress even in a country such as Britain are most marked in the lowlands when flat or undulating land makes mechanization possible. Thus what matters is the mapping of different types of terrain or land forms on a geomorphological basis. The Japanese have recognized this: in their country there is a very sharp contrast between the plains where rice can be grown and the surrounding hills where different degrees of slope are controlling factors in land use.

It so happens that some of the most significant characters of soils are sometimes manifest at the surface, and so apparent from a study of air photographs. Thus saline incrustations in arid lands stand out very clearly; so do areas of waterlogging. In the aerial survey of Western Pakistan it was accordingly possible to prepare a soil reconnaissance map of considerable value. Unwisely some enthusiasts have declared the possibility of making complete soil surveys from the air, which cannot in fact be done.

Soil Texture

Although with the modern chemicalization of agriculture it is possible to counteract salinity by application of gypsum (calcium sulphate) and to alter textures by dressings of lime and some recently developed soil conditioners, it is still true that what matters most is the texture of the surface layers. We are taken right back to the old county soil maps of Britain, to the soil texture maps of the Geological Survey, and this leads to another consideration.

THE PEDOLOGICAL PARADOX

Undoubtedly the best texture for a good all-purpose agricultural soil is that of a loam: a mixture of fine sand or silt with a moderate proportion of clay to hold moisture and to prevent moisture and fertilizers draining through the soil too rapidly. In the farmer's language, a coarse sandy soil is hungry. Stones are apt to prevent the proper development of root systems. From time immemorial this significance of soil texture has been recognized. The ancient Egyptians knew the virtues of Nile alluvium; the Anglo-Saxon settlers in Britain sought the loam terrains. Where such soils do not exist they have often been made. In China the farmer on heavy clay land would exchange a few thousand baskets of his soil for an equal number from a neighbour on sandy land. Labour was available and once the mixture is made it is permanent, or at least lasts a very long time. In Britain farmers on light superficial sands sought a pit where they could dig clay or marl to spread over their land. To this day hundreds of tons of sea sand (also rich in lime from shell fragments) is carted from the coasts of North Cornwall to be spread over the heavy clay soils which cover much of the nearby country. In wet regions—and this applies to much of Britain—soils are apt to be acid and need dressing with some form of lime. In olden days many chalk pits were opened and farmers carted chalk to dress their clay lands. After 50 or even 100 years the advantages of this chalking are still apparent, whereas the effects of modern liming last only a year or two, dressing with powdered limestone rather longer.

Although the importance of texture is known, it is strange that with all the powerful earth-moving machinery now available no attempts have been directed towards making a good agricultural soil by mixing sands, silts, clays and limestone in right proportions. What a tremendous opportunity for a crowded country where good agricultural land is vital!

There are however at the present day opposing trends. Many modern practices take little heed of the desirability of building up a soil. In the old days of basin irrigation, an annual layer of silt was deposited over the cultivated fields of Egypt; with modern perennial irrigation from great reservoirs only water is led on to the fields. In Britain modern tile-drainage of fields and the deepening and straightening of rivers allows mud and silt to be swept out to sea in contrast to the old system of warping, which led the material gently to settle and build up land water-covered at flood seasons.

THE PEDOLOGICAL PARADOX

An Australian Pioneer

Work at present going on in Australia is particularly interesting in this connection. The arid interior, two-thirds of the 3,000,000 square miles of the continent, is of little value, and the better watered fringe presents many problems. For example, there are very large areas of very poor shaley soils, or light land developed on poor granitic waste. An Australian engineer turned farmer, Mr. P. A. Yeomans, has developed a very interesting system of management of such land. His system he has called the Keyline Plan since it stems basically from a key-point in a valley, where the swift upper course of a stream gives place to a slower plains course. In other words he finds first a significant break of slope in a valley which may or may not correspond with a knick-point in the stream. From this point irrigation ditches sloping gently away from the key-point are dug on either side. This constitutes the Keyline. Other irrigation channels are constructed parallel. The general idea is to allow the water, controlled if required by an earth-dammed reservoir at the key-point and elsewhere, to escape slowly along the almost parallel drains and from them to seep gently down the hillsides. There it provides the right hydrological conditions for the rapid development of a soil flora and fauna. Yeomans has shown how, given the right physical conditions, these organisms (and earthworms which soon appear in large numbers) will build up an excellent soil from unpromising material in a matter of months, or at least in a year or two. The two bases for the work—a detailed understanding of the geomorphology and the creation of a soil climate and hydrology—are both scientifically sound. Other factors enter into the work, such as the intelligent use of trees, which the Australian farmer, like other pioneers, has long regarded as natural enemies to be cleared away. When I visited the pioneer farms at Nevallan some 45 miles north-west of Sydney in 1957 I found the demonstration of what had been done so convincing that it was impossible not to see the enormous possibilities of the extension of the Keyline Plan to other parts of the world—at very little cost.

This may lead us to question much of the current attitude to soil erosion and soil conservation.

Is Soil Erosion a World Problem?

Even to pose such a question sounds today remarkably like heresy.

THE PEDOLOGICAL PARADOX

Yet little more than a generation ago soil erosion had scarcely been heard of. Our universities giving first-year courses in geology devoted much time and attention to the processes of erosion and denudation; sixth-formers in their physical geography learnt of the inevitable lowering of the land surface by those agents whose significance Lyell had so studiously delineated a century before. But that was geological erosion and little was said about soil, though it must be obvious that any surface layer of soil must be removed before the rocks below can be attacked.

Soil Erosion

Every geologist is familiar with the erosion cycle. No sooner has an area of land been raised above sea-level than it becomes subject to the erosive forces of Nature. The rain beats down on the ground and washes away the finer particles, sweeping them into rivulets and then into rivers and out to sea. The frost freezes the rain water in cracks of the rocks and breaks up even the hardest of the constituents of the earth's crust. Blocks of rock dislodged at high levels are brought down by the force of gravity. Alternate heating and cooling of bare rock surfaces causes their disintegration. In the arid regions of the world the wind is a powerful force in removing material from one area to another. All this is natural. But Nature has also provided certain defensive forces. Bare rock surfaces are in due course protected by soil, itself dependent initially on the weathering of the rocks. Slowly but surely, different types of soil with differing 'profiles' evolve, the main types depending primarily on the climate. The protective soil covering, once it is formed, is held together by the growth of vegetation. Grass and herbaceous plants, with long, branching tenuous roots, hold firmly together the surface particles. The same is true with the forest cover. The heaviest tropical downpours beating on the leaves of the giant trees reach the ground only as spray, gently watering the surface layers and penetrating along the long passages provided by the roots to the lower levels of the soil. The soil, thus protected by grass, herbs, or trees, furnishes a quiet habitat for a myriad varied organisms—earth-worms that importantly modify the soil, bacteria, active in their work of converting fallen leaves and decaying vegetation into humus and food for the growing plants. Chemical action is constantly taking place; soil acids attack mineral particles and salt in solution move from one layer in the soil to another.

We may sum this up by saying that under the natural vegetative cover,

THE PEDOLOGICAL PARADOX

the soil profile proper to the climatic conditions and the parent rock substances gradually develops. It is a long process, and in many areas there has not been sufficient time, in the geological sense, for completion of the process; the soils are 'immature'.

Now let us consider what happens when man, the pioneer, comes along. He ploughs up the natural grasslands. He removes the numerous branching roots that have held together the surface particles, so that they are now easily moved by the action of rain and wind. In ploughing he has mixed together the surface layers and provided his crops with a medium in which they can grow and develop and in which natural plant food is present in varying degree, or which may be supplemented by animal or chemical manures. But he has also exposed the soil to the action of the atmosphere. In some parts of the world exposure is useful: in a cold climate the breaking up of the clods of clay by frost action is beneficial. At the other extreme, as we have already pointed out, in tropical climates, by exposure to the atmosphere such rapid chemical action may have been set up that the natural plant food in the soil is quickly destroyed.

Broadly speaking, the position is worse when the natural vegetation is forest. Not only does man, the pioneer, rob the soil of its source of humus, the fallen leaves, but he exposes a soil quite unused to the direct rays of the sun and the direct fall of the rain to the immediate influence of both. For example, much of the upland and west coast of Scotland was once forested with the beautiful Scots fir (*Pinus sylvestris*). The heavy rain, falling on the close pine-woods, trickled gradually to the ground and soaked into the soil. Much was evaporated from the leaves, and the floor of the forest, covered with pine needles, remained comparatively dry, supporting a sparse cover or undergrowth of various shade-loving plants or low shrubs such as bilberry and heather. When the forests were cut down, the heavy rain fell straight on to the surface soil more rapidly than it could drain away. Especially where there was no steep slope the water was held up, and moisture-loving plants began to flourish, particularly sphagnum, or bog moss. Once the sphagnum was established it acted as a sponge. True, it prevented soil erosion, but it grew and grew until great thicknesses of moss blanketed the whole countryside. Thus huge stretches of bog land, that known to the botanists as 'blanket bog', extending over wide areas of Scotland and Ireland, are directly due to man's action.[1]

[1] See J. W. Watson, 'Forest or Bog: Man the Deciding Factor', *Scottish Geographical Magazine*, Vol. 55, 1939, pp. 148–61.

THE PEDOLOGICAL PARADOX

A different, perhaps more familiar, example is seen in many of the hilly parts of the south-eastern United States. The originally forested slopes were cleared by the pioneers for timber or for the creation of farmlands. The bare soil was left unprotected; heavy downpours of rain rapidly washed it away and one gets the familiar feature of gully erosion and of hillsides literally swept bare of any vestige of soil. But of course this example could be multiplied elsewhere in the United States and all over the world. No more heart-breaking story of man's improvidence is told than in the barren, eroded hills of China, land of famine.

Now what is the present situation in the United States? Dr. Hugh H. Bennett supplies the following estimate from the Soil Conservation Service of the Department of Agriculture (1934 survey, supplemented by more recent detailed surveys); lands no longer used for cultivated crops, except in small, scattered areas, owing to severe erosion, 100 million acres; total area of crop and grazing land seriously affected by erosion, 282 million acres; land moderately affected by erosion, 775 million acres. Thus 1,157,000,000 are more or less seriously affected by erosion out of a total for the continental United States of 1,905,000,000 acres.[1]

When one bears in mind that the greater part of the area to which these figures refer has been settled only some hundred years or less, we get a glimpse of the incredible destruction that can be caused by man-induced soil erosion.

The preceding paragraphs are taken from my previous book. At that time, less than ten years ago, it was being widely stated that because of soil erosion land was being lost to cultivation more rapidly than compensating land was being regained, and that mankind was moving towards the position when it would starve itself by its own stupid actions. Everywhere it was said the soil was being 'mined' for the sake of 'cheap' food. It so happened that some bad seasons when soil erosion was very marked coincided with the Great Depression of the nineteen-thirties in the United States. Remedial measures were closely identified with F. D. Roosevelt's fight against the Depression. Such books as *The Rape of the Earth* (American title *Vanishing Lands*) by G. V. Jacks and R. O. Whyte gave a world-wide survey of the 'greatest scourge the world has ever known'. Others, such as Fairfield Osborn's *Our Plundered Planet*, served to put over the ideal of conservation with a bang.

It is not my purpose here to deal with the wide range of the now established soil conservation practices—with the development of con-

[1] See also above, p. 67.

THE PEDOLOGICAL PARADOX

tour ploughing and strip cropping, with the selection of trees and grasses for planting on slopes, with the prevention of gullying, the blocking of stream courses.

I am however concerned with two aspects of the present position. The first is that I believe the time has come when we should review critically some basic concepts of what has now become 'orthodox' conservation. We cannot prevent geological erosion, we should not try, but we may control it to our advantage.

The second is that we should cease to be so obsessed with our superior knowledge, with our supposed monopoly of 'know-how' that we should be unwilling to think afresh and perhaps learn from those we regard as our inferiors. Admittedly there are parts of the world where the native peoples know little of the arts of cultivation; but also there are lands where native cultivators have a good deal to teach us.

In the wetter parts of West Africa, 'basin' cultivation is widely practised. Let us look at the operation in a little more detail.[1] In the first place, the forest is cleared over small areas only, so that if erosion does attack a field, its incidence is limited. There is no clear felling over large tracts. When the small area to be cultivated is selected, the soil is carefully hoed up by hand into a series of ridges, and the furrows between are crossed at intervals, say six to ten feet, by transverse ridges. If a very heavy downpour of rain occurs, some of the soil will be washed from the ridges, but it will not go farther than into the little basins containing the water. Incidentally, under such an arrangement it is possible to grow two types of crops, one moisture-loving and one which prefers a better-drained soil on the ridges. This system of peasant cultivation is laborious in the extreme, but we may recall that the principle was considered as a solution of soil erosion problems in the United States, and that a special type of plough, the 'basin lister', was designed to create similar little basins by mechanical means.

Let us take another instance from West Africa. The European or North American visitor to Ghana may find it difficult to know when he is on the cultivated part of a native farm and when he is in the surrounding jungle. The whole seems to him to be a tangle of weeds and of odd trees, and he longs to teach the peasant the virtues of a clean farm and of weed control. But in fact the weeds act as a protection to the soil, and replacement of the 'dirty' farm in Ghana by a clean-swept European model would quickly result in loss of soil and soil fertility. Clearly the

[1] For illustrations see L. Dudley Stamp, 'Land Utilization and Soil Erosion in Nigeria,' *Geographical Review*, XXVIII (1938), pp. 32–45.

THE PEDOLOGICAL PARADOX

object here should be to develop the system by substituting a cover crop of value in itself, for useless weeds.

For another example we may turn to the Peruvian Andes and the ancient system of terracing, the *andenes*, that made productive steep slopes where no modern system of cultivation could hope to succeed. We know, too, how, from the point of view of land conservation, the shifting cultivation common in much of tropical Africa is wasteful of land and gives but small returns, but is conservative of both the soil and soil fertility.

Lessons from Pakistan

Although there may be thus some confusion of thought concerning the relationship between soil erosion and land conservation, in practice many of the works undertaken do in fact fit in with the natural cycle of erosion and deposition. This is well illustrated from reclamation works of recent decades in Western Pakistan in the Thal area (between the Indus and the Jhelum). There the foothills of the Salt Range are of unconsolidated sands and silts with some clays of the later Tertiaries, whilst some of the older alluvium is at a sufficient elevation to promote deep gullying. The result is a wide stretch of badlands developed on deposits, often wrongly referred to as 'soils', which are essentially good soil-forming material. Some areas of the badlands have been bulldozed into roughly level areas which is, in reality, hastening the natural development of a sub-aerial peneplane. Suitably provided with irrigation water, this new land is cultivable. In the natural state 'periodic' flooding of the 'chos' sweep vast quantities of the fine sediments disastrously over wide courses and so into the Indus, where the coarser material is piled up as sandbanks, the finer swept down to build up the delta in its seaward expansion. The bunds of earth, with masonry spillways, are designed to catch this sediment and so to build up, artificially, flood plains of rich alluvium or what are really inland deltas. It is broadly what the Egyptians did for thousands of years in their basin irrigation. Surplus water is allowed to escape down the spillways, its volume lessened, its channel controlled, its burden of suspended sediment greatly reduced. The water joining the main river is thus without the sediment which in a few years would choke and ruin the great dams at Sukkur and in the delta. There the water has a different function. It is to be led over the already existing alluvial flats, needing only irrigation water to supplement the negligible rainfall and to convert them into

THE PEDOLOGICAL PARADOX

rich farmland. The central core of the whole scheme is not the prevention of soil or geological erosion in the distant hills, but the trapping of the material where it can be made to build up worthwhile land and the consequent release of silt-free water.

The paradoxes which have been briefly mentioned in this chapter should serve to suggest that in few branches of knowledge is there greater need for some careful rethinking as there is in the study of soils and soil management. Without doubt certain current practices are self-contradictory; some established conservation methods need to be drastically revised.

VII

THE MEASUREMENT OF LAND RESOURCES AND FARMING EFFICIENCY

In Chapter III it was pointed out that large areas of the earth's surface which appear to have the physical conditions of a terrain, climate and soil to encourage human settlement and agricultural development remain sparsely peopled. It was further pointed out that, on a basis of world average, it needs the produce of a little over one acre to support one person. Whilst it is easy to say, therefore, that some countries are 'under-populated' in the sense that they could support, from their own land resources, a larger population, it is much more difficult to say if or when a country is fully populated and still more to venture to say it is 'over-populated'.

The Concept of Over-Population

Like many concepts which seem obvious and simple enough when first considered, the concept of over-population proves to be extremely difficult and complex when analysed in detail. It is certainly possible to conceive a country so crowded with people that the term 'over-populated' seems justified and on this basis a city-state such as the island of Hong Kong would seem to qualify. In general, however, what one implies is a country unable to produce sufficient food on its own territory to feed its people. In this sense, as Britain is able to produce only some 55 per cent of the food consumed, it could be called over-populated. But is it? Even on the basis of food production? If we liked to change our food habits, live mainly on bread and potatoes and farm with greater intensity irrespective of cost, we could no doubt feed our 50 million people on our own resources. Over-population is thus linked with standard of living, dietary habits, type and intensity of farming.

Type of farming is particularly important. In tropical Africa for example an acre of land can produce the limited food needs of the average African. But the type of farming will most likely be the so-called shifting cultivation of bush fallowing or land rotation. A patch of land cultivated for, say, three years is allowed to rest by reverting to bush, but takes fifteen years to regain its fertility. Thus the one acre to support one person is really six, five years being in fallow. Many years ago I attempted to show, on this basis, that considerable parts of Nigeria[1] were over-populated and that land was being impoverished by reducing the period of fallow. More recently[2] I have attempted to show that England and Wales with only between 2 and 5 million people was probably 'over-populated' over considerable periods of the Middle Ages according to the level of production, and type of farming then in use. It has been pointed out that some diets are immensely more extravagant of land than others, but the broad general tendency in the new Agricultural Revolution is for land to be used more intensively. The world average of 1·1 or 1·2 acres to support one person is in course of being rapidly lowered. Thus a country which is over-populated on present levels of production might have a huge surplus with improved farming. This is notably the position in India. If India's crop yields were raised by the use of methods already known and widely applied, even to the levels of world average, there would remain a huge population, but a well-fed one, and it might be difficult to talk of over-population.

We are led to consider a number of distinct, if related, topics—such as the measurement of agricultural efficiency, the carrying capacity of land in terms of people, and the optimum farming population.

The Measurement of Agricultural Efficiency

Before we can assess under-development, we need some measure of the efficiency of existing production. We must at the outset appreciate the fact, not by any means fully recognized, that there are at least three entirely different approaches to the subject. The first approach regards efficiency as indicated by output per unit area, the second measures efficiency in terms of the output of labour, that is per man-hour; and the third is the input-output ratio and the profitability of farming measured in terms of the return for the sum total of human effort. The

---

[1] L. D. Stamp: 'Land Utilization in Nigeria'. *Geog. Rev.*, New York, 28, 1938.
[2] L. D. Stamp: *Man and the Land*. Collins *New Naturalist Series*, London, 1955, pp. 92–94.

THE MEASUREMENT OF LAND RESOURCES

issue is further complicated when the value of output is introduced, especially with the absurdities that result if values are expressed according to the present arbitrary rates of exchange between the world's currencies. A nearer approximation is reached when values are measured in terms of real wages.

In a world short of food it is surely clear that what matters in many, perhaps most, countries is the actual amount of food produced, so, making some allowance for quality, the higher the output per unit area the greater the efficiency of the farmer. In the tables which were given for wheat, rye, maize, rice and sugar cane in Chapter IV the world average (excluding U.S.S.R.) of yield per hectare and per acre in metric tons is given for two quinquennia, before and after the Second World War, of 1934–38 and 1948–52 as well as for 1956. Taking wheat as typical for mid-latitude cereals in each of these periods, Denmark, Holland and Belgium are at the top, followed closely by the United Kingdom and so, on this showing, these countries are the most efficient producers in the world. Though they have greatly improved Canada, the United States and Argentina are relatively inefficient producers; Spain, Pakistan and India disastrously so.

But to base our judgement on one crop, wheat, is obviously dangerous, and a number of attempts have been made to combine the yields of several crops. Many years ago the late Professor Ellsworth Huntington and Professor Samuel Van Valkenburg constructed the two maps of Europe reproduced as Figs. 28 and 29 using the eight widely raised crops—wheat, rye, barley, oats, corn, potatoes, sugar beet and hay; for each crop the yield per acre for Europe as a whole was called 100 and the yield in each country calculated accordingly. The outstanding fact is that the countries of north-western Europe, headed by Belgium, Holland, Denmark and England reached the highest level of more than 150 per cent. Conversely, in the countries of Mediterranean and eastern Europe, the intensity of agriculture drops below 100, the lowest recorded being 57 per cent in Greece. The second map illustrates the reliability of the harvest—largely a reflection of climatic conditions.

Professor M. G. Kendall approached the subject as a mathematical problem. Taking the acre yields of ten leading crops in each of the forty-eight administrative counties in England for four selected years, he tried out four coefficients—productivity, ranking, money value, and starch equivalent or energy. His first coefficient involves mathematics beyond the power of the non-expert and the use of a calculating machine. As Kendall himself said: 'The labour required prompted me

THE WORLD'S LANDS

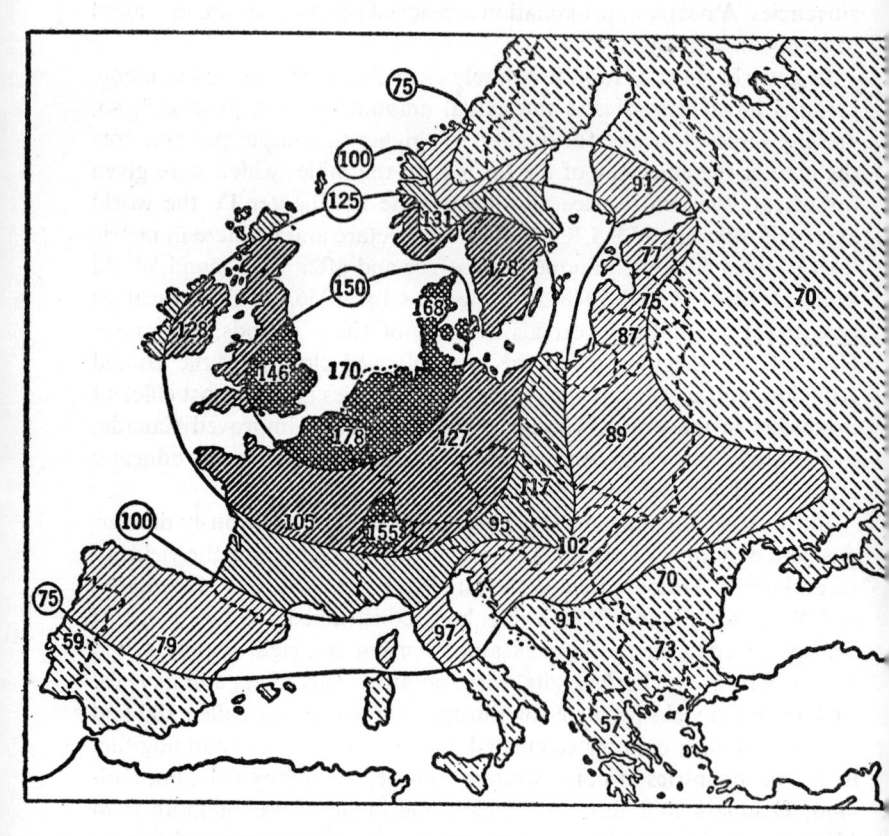

Fig. 28

Intensity of agriculture: 100 is the yield per acre for eight crops for Europe as a whole. (Reproduced by permission from *Europe* by S. Van Valkenburg and Ellsworth Huntington, published by John Wiley & Sons, 1935)

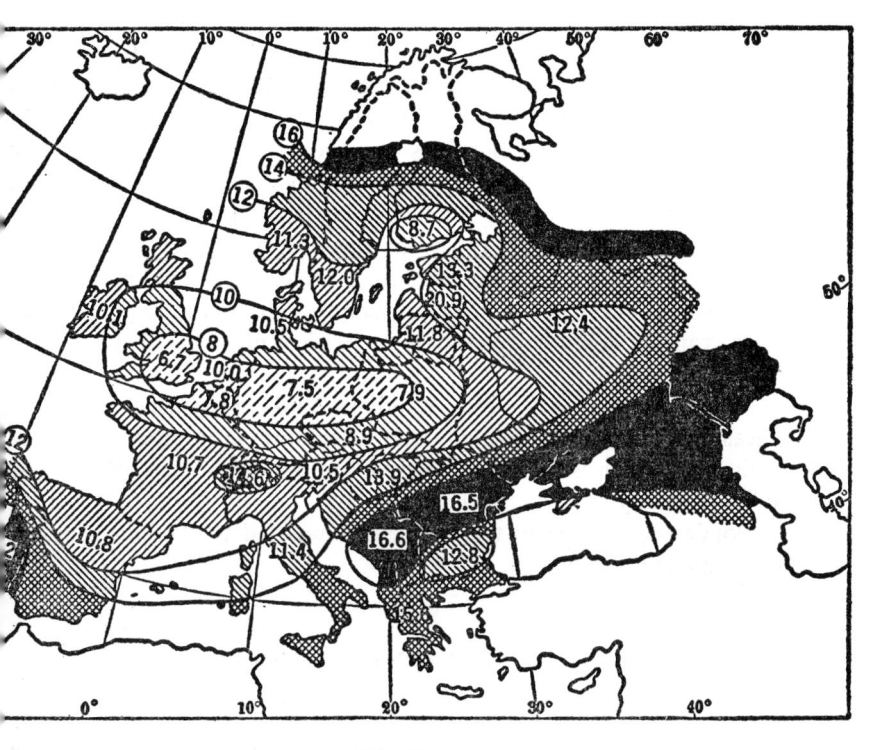

Fig. 29

Variability of crop yields expressed as average percentage of departure from the normal for 1927–33. (Reproduced by permission from *Europe* by S. Van Valkenburg and Ellsworth Huntington, published by John Wiley & Sons, 1935)

to look for a coefficient which, though perhaps of doubtful theoretical meaning, might lead to similar results in practice.' He accordingly devised his 'ranking coefficient'. Kendall's attempt to rank the English counties actually gave some curious results because he was compelled to ignore pasture land, so important in the English farming economy.

I attempted to apply Kendall's method internationally by selecting twenty countries and nine crops—wheat, rye, barley, oats, corn, potatoes, sugar beet, beans, and peas. The selected crops are grown in nearly all the countries, but for some, averages for certain crops only could be used. The method is simple. For each crop the countries are placed in order of output per acre, that is from 1 to 20. The place occupied by each country is then averaged. If one country were at the top of every list it would have a ranking coefficient of one; if a country were at the bottom of every list (presuming each country to grow all the nine crops) it would have a ranking coefficient of twenty. Table XIX is the result.

What, we may ask, does Kendall's ranking coefficient actually measure? The answer is simply that it measures crop productivity per unit area, which is the result partly of natural advantages of soil and climate, partly of farming efficiency.

Pondering further on the problem, I was led to the concept of a Standard Nutrition Unit.

A Standard Nutrition Unit

The fundamental difficulty in measuring efficiency of farming output in different parts of the world is obviously the range and variety of crops. As noted above, Huntington and Van Valkenburg used eight widely raised crops for Europe; I used nine in adapting Kendall's Ranking Coefficient for international comparisons.

It is however possible to convert the production of *any* crop into starch-equivalent or better into Nutrition Calories which then can be used to measure output in terms of what has been called above 'human fuel'. The great advantage of the Nutrition Calorie is that one can then compare directly, say, a wheat diet with a rice diet or a mixed diet of almost any source. This was the approach I used in my Presidential Address to the International Geographical Congress at Rio in 1956.[1]

[1] L. D. Stamp, 'The Measurement of Land Resources,' *Geog. Rev.*, New York, XLVIII, 1958, 1–15.

THE MEASUREMENT OF LAND RESOURCES

TABLE XIX

TWENTY SELECTED COUNTRIES IN ORDER OF FARMING EFFICIENCY

(Kendall's Ranking Coefficient)

1934–38		1946	
Belgium	2·2	Belgium	2·3
Denmark	2·6	Denmark	2·4
Netherlands	2·9	Netherlands	2·4
Germany	4·3	New Zealand	4·2
Britain	4·7	Britain	4·8
Ireland	4·7	Ireland	5·3
New Zealand	5·8	Egypt	6·2
Egypt	6·3	Germany	7·6
Austria	7·2	United States	8·2
France	9·2	France	9·0
Japan	10·4	Canada	9·1
Italy	12·0	Austria	11·2
United States	12·0	Chile	11·5
Canada	12·3	Argentina	12·4
Spain	12·6	China	12·7
Chile	12·9	Italy	12·7
China	13·6	Japan	14·1
Argentina	14·3	Spain	14·2
Australia	16·0	India	17·0
India	17·8	Australia	17·2

First it is to be noted that the farmer thinks in terms of an annual harvest, or at least his production per annum, even when there is double or treble cropping. On the other hand human beings, whether they consume their daily intake of food in one, two, three or more meals, think essentially in terms of days. . . . Give us this day our daily bread. A number of preliminary calculations convinced me that a very useful, if apparently arbitrary, unit was 1,000,000 Nutrition Calories per annum in terms of farm production. The output of wheat or rice per acre can be converted simply from bushels or kilograms or any other unit used in measuring output into Calories. Whether the output is from yams, sweet potatoes, maize or bananas the total per acre can still be calculated. In any case or with any crop, however, not all the 1,000,000 Calories is directly available for human food. There is a loss in initial preparation—the milling of grain with varied extraction rates —and some loss in cooking or final preparation for the table. In getting an overall picture allowance must be made for seed. Although obviously, especially in so-called advanced or civilized countries there is a very

THE MEASUREMENT OF LAND RESOURCES

considerable wastage of food after it is cooked and brought to the table (probably reaching a very considerable percentage in a country like the United States) allowance for such waste is arbitrary and difficult. Taking however the general range of extraction rates and known losses in food preparation[1] a loss of 10 per cent would seem to be a close approximation to the truth. Thus the Standard Nutrition Unit of 1,000,000 Calories *produced* become one of 900,000 Calories per year consumed or available for consumption. This is 2,460 Calories a day.

How does this compare with the desirable or optimum intake? The British Medical Association carried out an exhaustive inquiry based on all available sources and in the official *Manual of Nutrition* (4th edition, Ministry of Agriculture, Fisheries and Food, London, 1955) published a series of recommended dietary allowances of Calories, proteins, calcium, iron, vitamin A, vitamin B_1, riboflavin, nicotinic acid (niacin) and vitamin C for people of different ages and occupations in both sexes. The tables show a range in desirable Calorie intake among adults from 2,100 a day for a woman in a sedentary occupation to 4,250 for a man doing active manual work, and among children from 800 a day for infants under 1 year to 3,400 for teenage boys. The average of the different categories works out at 2,540 Calories a day; if the age structure of the population and the range of occupations were taken into account, it would be somewhat lower. In other words this average, for the weight and height of the people living under the climatic conditions of north-western Europe, is almost precisely the 2,460 Calories a day postulated for the Standard Nutrition Unit. Precisely the same figure of 1,000,000 Calories a year farm production was reached in an entirely different way by James Wyllie and was used by him to determine the *per capita* consumption of food in the United Kingdom, 1936–50.[2]

It must be pointed out that the Standard Nutrition Unit, or SNU, is not a satisfactory unit unless it also satisfies certain other conditions.

First, it must be based upon a sufficient variety of foodstuffs to give an adequate protein intake. The *Manual of Nutrition* gives an average of 80 grams (rather less than 3 oz.) a day and suggests an essential balance between animal and vegetable proteins. In view of the large proportion of vegetarians in some countries (probably 90 per cent of the 480 million people of India and Pakistan for example) the latter

[1] See the elaborate tables published by FAO, *Food Composition Tables for International Use*, United Nations Food and Agriculture Organization, Washington, 1949.

[2] James Wyllie, *Land Requirements for the Production of Human Foods*, University of London, Wye College, 1954.

THE MEASUREMENT OF LAND RESOURCES

proviso is not of universal application. It is perhaps sufficient to say that a SNU must include adequate protein.

Second, it must also be presumed that essential quantities of 'protective foods' are included. In essence this requires a mixed diet and is only likely to be a serious issue where there is an excessive reliance on one staple, e.g. rice or potatoes. In *The State of Food and Agriculture, 1958*, p. 120, the experts of FAO quoted results of investigations on diets in different parts of Nigeria, French Togoland and the Ivory Coast. The actual intake per day is compared with 'estimated requirements' in Calories, protein, carbohydrates, fats, calcium, vitamin A, vitamin B_1 (thiamin), riboflavin, niacin (nicotinic acid) and ascorbic acid. Few, if any, of the diets satisfied all these requirements.

It must further be pointed out that the SNU is based on conditions prevailing in north-west Europe, though broadly applicable to other parts of mid-latitudes where people are of European stock. In those parts of the world where the average height and weight of people is less, an adequate diet would average less than 2,460 Calories a day, e.g. in India. Though some allowance must be made for climate, exactly how much is difficult to determine. Work in the Canadian Army suggests that the addition for a cold climate is related more to weight of clothing than to outside temperatures, and some interesting observations were made in Antarctica during the International Geophysical Year, notably by Sir Vivian Fuchs's Trans-Antarctic Party. It would seem safe, however, to assume some deduction can be made in caloric requirements in hot climates. The work of Dr. Shafi in northern India, quoted below, suggests that an actual intake of 2,000 Calories a day, equivalent to a farm production of little over 800,000 per annum, is adequate. It is difficult to use some very high figures of apparent consumption, notably in the United States, because, as already noted, of the very large proportion of food prepared but in fact thrown away.

In deducting 10 per cent from farm production it must also be noted that the deduction in countries with a low yield must be greater to allow for seed.

The Use of the Standard Nutrition Unit

A number of different uses can be made of the unit of 1,000,000 Calories of production.

In the first place where it is possible to measure actual production and consumption one can then show how far the food intake of a given

THE MEASUREMENT OF LAND RESOURCES

community falls short of the standard. It may sometimes be possible to do this on a national basis where there is a reasonably accurate estimate of total production. In countries where statistics might be expected to be fairly complete there are often many disturbing factors. In Britain, for example, land of animal-lovers, how much food goes to the feeding of 4,000,000 dogs, over 5,000,000 cats and 6,000,000 cage birds? It is in any case difficult to separate the proportions of such foodstuffs as potatoes, oats, barley, many vegetables and roots which are for direct human consumption and the proportions which are fed to animals. The imports of foodstuffs are also complex. The problem is simpler in a country which is broadly self-contained in foodstuffs. Perhaps some of the most accurate measurements yet made are those for a dozen villages in northern India with a subsistence agriculture, and where the people are vegetarians. The investigations were made by Dr. Muhammed Shafi, and I have given his main results in my Presidential Address already quoted. He found a production based on a wide range of crops equivalent to a daily intake between 1,828 and 2,175 Calories a day. Where the intake fell below 2,000 there was obvious evidence of malnutrition. The villagers instinctively build up their caloric intake from whatever sources are available. In two cases more than a fifth of the total was made up of local sugar dissolved in water to make a sweet drink.

In the second place, one has a measure of farming efficiency in the sense of determining the area of land needed under cultivation to support one person—in other words the 'carrying capacity' of the land in terms of population. But this varies enormously according to the type of diet. Some diets—for example those with a large proportion of meat and milk—are very extravagant of land whilst cereal diets, especially rice, are economical of land. This aspect is more fully considered later. We may note that even among vegetable staples there is a considerable range in the caloric value of a given weight of food. With cereal flour, as purchased retail, the average is near 360 Calories per 100 grams and the range only from about 330 to 370, whereas potatoes are about 70 Calories per 100 grams.

In the third place, within a given area such as a small country where climate and types of farming are fairly uniform, it should prove possible to get a little nearer an accurate measure of qualities of land (see page 117), that is the range of land capability classes of potential production.

THE MEASUREMENT OF LAND RESOURCES

Some International Comparisons

By converting yields of the various food crops grown into SNUs it is possible to measure and compare intensity of production from one country to another. This I have attempted to do for the countries shown in Table XX. The table is obviously incomplete: in many cases data do not exist upon which one can estimate either potentially cultivable land or Calorie output from land already cultivated.

Table XX affords a measure of the 'carrying capacity' of farmed land in terms of human beings it can support. On each acre of farmed land—essentially on a dietary base of rice, double or treble cropped where possible, beans, sweet potatoes and other high Calorie foods—Japan can produce 6 or 7 SNU or support that number of people per acre. Under American conditions, and with a meat-milk-fruit diet essentially extravagant of land, it takes some 2½ acres or more to produce one SNU or support one person. It we wish to stimulate an argument we can then say that Japanese agriculture is 15 to 18 times as efficient as American! Where land is in short supply the inference is justifiable. It leads one to think further on the carrying capacity of land and the potential productivity of the world.

The SNU is a useful unit with which to measure the actual output of farmed land. Provided, of course, the exact details of output are available, it could be used to measure the relative productivity of different types or qualities of land but, unfortunately, the essential details are rarely available. The classification of land according to actual or potential productivity rests precariously on a rather unsatisfactory basis.

A Scheme of Land Classification

When the British Government, alarmed at the loss to industry, housing and other forms of non-agricultural development, declared its intention of preserving as far as possible the good agricultural land of the country, the immediate difficulty arose that 'good' agricultural land had never been defined and had certainly never been mapped. I have recounted at length on several occasions[1] how an empirical 10-fold classification of land was drawn up and was later embodied in the Land Classification Map on the scale of 1: 625,000, published by the Ord-

[1] See *inter alia* L. D. Stamp, *The Land of Britain: Its Use and Misuse*, pp. 351–87.

THE MEASUREMENT OF LAND RESOURCES

TABLE XX

	Population millions Dec. 1958	Acreage per capita Total	Cultivable	Cultivated	SNU per cultivated area
World	2,850	12·0	4·0	1·1	0·75
United States	175·0	14·0	? 6·0	3·5	0·4
Brazil	63·3	41·0	30·0	1·0	1·3
United Kingdom	51·8	1·1	0·6	0·55	0·9
England and Wales	45·3	0·8	0·6	0·55	0·9
Canada	17·4	150·0	23·0	4·0	0·4
Australia	10·0	192·0	?	5·7	0·2
New Zealand	2·3	29·0	18·0	1·1 (8·6)[1]	
India	400·0	2·1	1·0	0·95	0·75
Pakistan	86·5	3·0	1·0	0·7	1·0
Ceylon	9·4	1·8		0·4	
Hong Kong	2·8	0·09	? 0·03	0·01	? 10·0
Singapore	1·77	0·08		0·02	
Malaya	6·8	4·8		0·8	
South Africa	14·5	21·0		1·5	
Rhodesia and Nyasaland	7·7	41·0			
Uganda	5·8	10·0	9·0	1·0	1·0
Kenya	6·4	23·0		0·63	
Tanganyika	9·3	25·0			
Nigeria	33·3	7·2		1·7	
Ghana	4·9	12·0		2·7	
Sierra Leone	1·9	9·4			
Gambia	0·29	8·9		1·9	
Cyprus	0·54	4·3		2·0	
Malta	0·33	0·24		0·15	
Jamaica	1·64	1·7		0·26	
Trinidad	0·80	1·5		0·51	
British Guiana	0·53	100·0		0·5	
Egypt	25·0		0·3	0·26	4·0
Burma	20·4	9·0	4·0	1·15	1·0
Japan	91·5	1·1		0·15	6·5
Holland	11·2	0·8	0·6	0·55	
Denmark	4·5	2·5	2·0	1·8	
France	44·5	3·3	2·0	1·8	0·6

[1] The figure in brackets includes sown grasses.

THE MEASUREMENT OF LAND RESOURCES

nance Survey for the Ministry of Town and Country Planning, now the Ministry of Housing and Local Government. The classification is as follows:

Category I—Good Quality Land

Highly productive when under good management. Land in this category has the following characteristics: Site: 1, not too elevated; 2, level, gently sloping or undulating; 3, favourable aspect. Soil: 1, deep; 2, favourable water conditions (actual or potential); 3, texture mostly loams but including some peats, sands, silts and clays.

1. *First-class Land Capable of Intensive Cultivation.* This land is especially good for the cultivation of foodstuffs for human consumption and hence designated 1(A) where A indicates 'arable'. The soils are deep and in texture mainly loams, but include some peats, fine sands, silts and loamy clays. Drainage must be free but not excessive, and the soils must not be excessively stony and must work easily at all seasons.

2. *Good General Purpose Farmland.* This is similar to No. 1, but has less depth of soil; presence of stones; occasional liability to drought or wetness; or some limitation of the seasons when soil works easily results in a restriction of the range of usefulness. When the conditions are such that the land is particularly suitable for arable cultivation the designation 2(A) may be used; when the conditions are such that sown grasses or permanent grassland are particularly suitable, the designation 2(AG) may be used, where G indicates 'grass'.

3. *First-class Land with Water Conditions Especially Favouring Grass.* This land is similar to 1(A) but as a result of a high permanent water table, liability to winter or occasional flooding, or somewhat heavier or less tractable soils, it is less suitable to arable cultivation than to grass. Such land may be converted into 1(A) by drainage or prevention of flooding, but this is a major operation. Designation is 3(G).

4. *Good but Heavy Land.* Although such land has soils of good depth and the natural fertility is often high, the soils, mostly the better clays and heavy loams, are heavy, and both the period of working and the range of possible crops are restricted. Designation is 4(AG).

Category II—Medium Quality Land

Land of only medium productivity even when under good management. Productivity is limited by reason of the unfavourable operation of one or more of the factors of site or soil character. Thus by reason of site: 1, high elevation; 2, steepness; 3, unfavourable aspect. By reason of soil: 1, shallowness; 2, defective water conditions. It is obvious that a wide range of conditions, indeed an almost endless combination of one, two, or more deleterious factors, is included in this major category.

5. *Medium Quality Light Land.* This is land defective by reason of lightness and, usually, shallowness of soil. The moderate elevation, relatively gentle slopes and consequent aspects are all satisfactory. There are several distinct types included within the category.

6. *Medium Quality General Purpose Farmland.* This is land defective primarily by reason of relief: steep slopes, elevation, varied aspect, and varied water conditions. In consequence soils are varied, often deficient by reason of stoniness, shallowness, heaviness, or in other ways. When studied in detail, such land may be resolved into a mosaic of small tracts or patches—perhaps only a part of a field in size—of land varying from group 1 to 10. Most land of group 6 is usually equally suitable for crops or grass, hence the designation 6(AG).

CATEGORY III—POOR QUALITY LAND

Land of low productivity by the extreme operation of one or more factors of site and soil. There are three main groups of 'extreme factors': extreme heaviness and/or wetness of soil giving poor quality heavy land or land in need of extensive drainage works; extreme elevation and/or ruggedness and/or shallowness of soil giving mountain moorland conditions; extreme lightness of soil with attendant drought and poverty giving poor quality light land. Several factors may combine to such an extent as to render the land agriculturally useless or almost so—such as shingle beaches or moving sand-dunes.

7. *Poor Quality Heavy Land.* This includes the more intractable clay lands and low-lying areas needing extensive drainage works before they can be rendered agriculturally useful. For convenience, undrained mosses or bogs have been included, though the soils they might eventually yield would not necessarily be heavy. The heavy clay lands tend to be in grass often rush-infested, hence the designation 7(G).

8. *Poor Quality Mountain Moorland.* The wide variety of land included in this group is apparent from the varied character of the natural or semi-natural vegetation by which it is clothed. General designation 8(H) where H indicates heathland or moorland.

9. *Poor Quality Light Land.* This group includes the so-called 'hungry'

or overdrained lands, usually overlying coarse sands or porous gravels and hence including both coastal sand-dunes and the inland sandy 'wastes' or heathland. Designation is 9(H).

10. *Poorest Land.* In its present state this land may be agriculturally useless, but this is not to deny possibilities of reclamation; salt marshes can be drained, sand-dunes fixed, and so on.

In Great Britain it is found the 'Good' lands occupy 38·7 per cent of the surface, the 'Medium' 26·3 and the 'Poor' 32·8, leaving 2·2 per cent as the built-over residue. In the whole of England and Wales and Scotland Type 1, First-class Lands, cover only 4·2 per cent of the surface—2,359,900 acres. They are indeed precious.

But what of the relative productivity of these different types? At a subsequent date[1] I introduced a PPU—Potential Production Unit—in an attempt to measure this. If one allows that Type 2, Good General Purpose Farm Land, has a productivity of 1 PPU per acre, if the technique and consequent productivity of farming were raised the rating would remain, though the value of a PPU would be raised. In other words, it is intended to be used for comparative purposes. The Ministry of Agriculture, Fisheries and Food already rates 10 acres of mountain moorland grazing (Type 8) as equivalent to 1 acre of improved farm land, i.e. it is given a rating of 0·1 PPU. On this basis it is tentatively suggested that the Medium Quality Lands (5 and 6) should have a rating of about 0·5, and the First-class Lands No. 1, a rating of 2. Simple calculations were carried out showing that the whole 37,270,000 acres of England and Wales had a total productive capacity of 27,610,000 PPU. The use of this unit in planning is of interest. Let us say a site for a new town requires 5,000 acres. If the site is chosen on First-class Land the country will lose 10,000 units of potential production. If it is sited on poor light sandy land (Type 9) the loss is only 500 units. This simple argument is of course complicated by the fact that, in open density housing, gardens remain to have a productive capacity.[2]

Land Capability Classes

The classification just described was evolved in a closely settled and intensively farmed country—Britain. The problem is rather different in sparsely populated or new lands. The many varied schemes of land

[1] L. D. Stamp, *The Under-Developed Lands of Britain*, Soil Association, 1954.
[2] R. H. Best and J. T. Ward, *The Garden Controversy*, Wye College, 1956.

THE MEASUREMENT OF LAND RESOURCES

classification were succinctly described by Dr. A. P. A. Vink in a paper which he presented to the International Seminar on Land Development for Agricultural Uses, 25th August to 12th September 1958, at Wageningen. He noted that we may distinguish at least six categories of classification:

1 in terms of inherent characteristics (Soil and Relief),
2 in terms of inherent qualities (Soil Quality classification),
3 in terms of present use (Soil Use),
4 in terms of use capabilities (Soil Suitability),
5 in terms of recommended use,
6 in terms of programme effectuation.

American workers have stressed Category 4—land capability classes—and one scheme widely used is the 8-fold scheme of the U.S. Soil Conservation Service:

I. Few limitations. Very good land from every standpoint.
II. Moderate limitations or risks of damage. Good land from all-round standpoint.
III. Severe limitations. Regular cultivation is possible if limitations are observed.
IV. Very severe limitations. Suited for occasional cultivation or for some kinds of limited cultivation.
V. Not suited for cultivation because of wetness, stones, overflows (flooding). Few limitations for grazing or forestry use.
VI. Too steep, stony, arid, wet, etc. for cultivation. Moderate limitations for grazing and forestry.
VII. Very steep, rough and wet, etc. Severe limitations for grazing or forestry.
VIII. Extremely rough, arid, swampy, etc. Not suited for cultivation or forestry. Suited for wild life, watersheds or recreation.

This is obviously a 'common-sense' classification, but it lacks any sure scientific background and is clearly very much a matter of individual subjective judgement. It reflects, too, the American attitude to grassland. In the British view, shared especially by parts of north-west Europe and countries like New Zealand, influenced by the British tradition, the individual farmer decides whether to plough and crop his land, to plough and grow grasses and fodder crops, or to manage it as permanent pasture, ploughed occasionally or never. The American view is to regard grassland or pasture simply as land (as in Category V above) not good enough for ploughing and cultivation.

THE MEASUREMENT OF LAND RESOURCES

The Stock-carrying Capacity of Land

The majority of cereal crops as well as most root crops such as potatoes, turnips and also green crops such as the *brassicae* can either be eaten direct by human beings or can be fed to domestic animals and eventually consumed as meat and milk. But animals are, speaking generally, inefficient converters and there is much loss on the way. Much more land is required to produce one SNU mainly of animal origin than one SNU of cereals. In other words when a nation, enjoying an increase in the standard of living, changes from a diet basically of bread or rice to one in which meat and milk play a large part much more land is needed. In such countries, notably Japan, where land is in desperately short supply, meat is a luxury not so much because of price as because the nation cannot afford the land for its production.

I have calculated that out of the improved farm acreage (crops and grass) in Britain only 20 per cent produces crops for direct human consumption against 80 per cent for the feeding of animals. It takes about 2·5 acres to support one stock unit. Whereas if Britons were content with a mainly bread and potato diet the land as at present farmed would produce 4 SNU per acre, with our mixed diet it produces rather less than 1 SNU.

There are, of course, certain compensating factors. Much land unsuitable for ploughing or cropping can be used for pasturing animals—this is true of the vast areas of what Americans often call range land (Category V of the above scheme) or that which appears in British statistics as rough grazing. Often the competition for such land is not between arable farming and grazing but between forestry and grazing. Much can be done, though comparatively little yet has been done, to increase the stock-carrying capacity of such land. Then certain animals, notably pigs and poultry, consume surplus food from homes and hotels which would otherwise be wasted. Even more important is the part played by animals in farm rotation, the maintenance of soil health and fertility.

Different types of land vary greatly in their stock-carrying capacity. It has become usual to express this in terms of 'livestock units'. One horse, one cow, one bull and one bullock are usually each considered as one livestock unit; a heifer or calf is 0·5; a ewe or ram, 0·14; a brood sow, 0·2; a fat pig, 0·1; and 100 adult poultry, one unit.

Well-managed grassland in Britain is considered able to support one grazing unit an acre throughout the year, and it seems permissible to use this as a standard. It can be used also in reverse, i.e. if a country has 10 million livestock units it would require the same number of acres, well managed, to support the number adequately. Increased acre yields resulting from good husbandry refer to grass, fodder crops, and animal-feeding stuffs as much as to foods for direct human consumption and so to increased stock-carrying capacity. True, this may not be reflected at once in increased meat or milk yields in proportion unless the character and quality of the stock is improved at the same time. Incidentally, as Britain has found with the improvement of hill pastures, increased yield of grass is wasted and the pastures rapidly deteriorate unless the animals are present to consume the increase.

Maximum Rural Densities

If the Japanese are able to produce 6 to 7 SNU per acre of cultivated land, equivalent to about 4,000 SNU per square mile, we may say that the cultivated land can support a population density of about 4,000 per square mile. If the producers were all entirely subsistence farmers, their style and intensity of farming would support that number actually on the ground. Many years ago F. H. King in his classic study of Chinese farming, *Farmers of Forty Centuries* (1927) argued that nowhere in the world did agriculture reach the same levels of intensive production as in the more favoured parts of China. In the Yangtse Delta for example rural densities reach 3,000 and 4,000—very close to the Japanese figure. In those parts of India such as the lower Ganges Valley and Delta where physical conditions are just as favourable lower yields and a less efficient farming result in maximum densities of 1,000–1,500 or even 2,000 in some of the districts of Eastern Bengal (Pakistan). The highly efficient peasant agriculture of Egypt results in 25,000,000 people being fed from the produce of 6,550,000 acres, with a large export of cotton also, so that the output is about 4 SNU per acre.

Turning to the intensively farmed countries of north-western Europe the average output in the Netherlands—wheat and other grains, vegetables, fruit and dairy produce leading—is probably twice that of Britain, or 2 SNU per acre, so that the agricultural land of the country supports at least a thousand persons per square mile. But Dutch agriculture is very far from subsistence farming and this leads us to quite another consideration—that of optimum rural densities.

THE MEASUREMENT OF LAND RESOURCES

Optimum Rural Densities

As we have seen, farming is everywhere becoming more and more a specialist business and the concern of an ever-decreasing proportion of the world's population. In order to secure maximum production from each acre of agricultural land, what labour force and what total resident population are needed? It may be impossible to give any answer to those questions which is of general application just as it is probably impossible to postulate an ideal size of holding. We can at least see what the actual position now is in the highly developed countries of north-western Europe.

In England the average size of a full-time holding is almost exactly 100 acres—with an average family of 3·15 which gives 20 persons per square mile. In the nineteen-thirties farm workers and their families increased this total to between 50 and 60 per square mile against 90 to 100 in 1871. But the new Agricultural Revolution has so far reduced the labour required that we may postulate now a total of 40 persons per square mile.

These considerations give us what I have called the Primary Rural Population. It is necessary for others to reside in the rural areas concerned in order to provide essential services—retail shopkeeping, transport, medical, educational and others without which the social structure of the countryside would collapse. The work of S. W. E. Vince[1] has shown that this Secondary Rural Population, as I have termed it, numbers about half the Primary Rural.

Except in areas of very highly productive and intensively farmed land, the increasing efficiency of the farmers has meant that a smaller Primary Population is needed than in the past and a smaller Secondary Rural to serve them. The total then becomes insufficient to maintain rural life with such essential services as doctor, clergy, schools and teachers, inns and recreational facilities. This is where the Adventitious Population—living in the country by choice—performs a vital function by maintaining a minimum density and especially the minimum number of children to support the village schools.[2]

Under the farming conditions of lowland Britain we thus get an 'optimum rural density' of the primary (40) and secondary (20) rural

---

[1] *Trans. and Papers, Inst. Brit. Geographers*, 1952, pp. 53–76.
[2] I have dealt with this problem in some detail in *The Land of Britain: Its Use and Misuse*, p. 448.

THE MEASUREMENT OF LAND RESOURCES

population of 60 per square mile of improved land. Taking the total area of improved land in England and Wales as 23,500,000 acres we reach the conclusion that this could be efficiently farmed under our existing systems by a primary rural population of 1,500,000 farmers, farm workers and their dependants, representing about 3·3 per cent only of the population. This number is actually greatly swollen because of the very large numbers of part-time and hobby farmers, including the many who add to pension or private income by becoming small-scale farmers or smallholders.

The main interest of this calculation, crude as it may be, is to suggest that the optimum farming population to secure the maximum production from the land is only a tiny fraction of the total population the produce of the land itself will support.

Some Wild Conclusions

It has been suggested earlier that the ecumene or habitable earth's surface is nearly four times that at present cultivated and cropped. If man could manage the varied climatic conditions and soils involved we may say that the world could support four times its present population without any advance in present yields. If one could conceive every part being brought up to the intensively cultivated lands in the favoured parts of Japan and China, and if mankind were content to live mainly on high Calorie vegetable foodstuffs, this result could be multiplied by six. Even allowing for physical space occupied by the vast number of human beings, the total carrying capacity of the earth's surface is thus many times its present population. For most efficient production the land would need to be cultivated by a comparatively small number of specialist farmers—probably under 5 per cent of the population.

It is difficult to suggest that world starvation may be just around the corner, however near it may be for some nations unless man-made barriers are torn down, for these figures take no account of the march of technical and scientific knowledge in land and soil management, crop and animal husbandry, or of the possibilities of the vast uncultivated seas.

VIII

THE BALANCE OF POWER

The richest man in the world in 1957 was probably the ruler of Kuwait. In that year he received an income from oil profits of £93,600,000—without even income tax to worry about. Yet oil was found in his desert territory only in 1938 and prior to that the impoverished sheikdoms of the Persian Gulf could have been classed as amongst the least developed parts of the world.

This is but one example of how a source of power—oil—may completely upset the 'balance of power' in another sense from that in which that phrase is commonly used.

A source of power or energy is essential to all human life. Among primitive peoples a fire for cooking involves some sort of fuel and except in tropical regions some sort of fuel is also needed for heating the house. The primitive forge for smelting iron requires fuel; at a slightly more advanced stage the windmill and the water-mill enter into the economy. The progress from under-development to development in a nation is sometimes considered as almost synonymous with industrialization, involving a switch from hand labour to the use of power on a large scale.

In primitive societies the commonest fuel is wood, either consumed as such or made into charcoal. Especially where other fuels are scarce, wood may continue to be an important source of power even in advanced societies—as evidenced by wood-burning locomotives on many railways, and wood-burning steamers. Brazil has established a modern iron and steel industry using, at Monlevade, only charcoal made from wood. In that case a million acres of land have been reserved for the production of the fuel needed—an indication of the great demands on land where modern industry relies on wood as a source of power. In most of the great timber-producing countries extensive use is made of sawmill waste: whilst the disposal of sawdust by simply burning it as a waste product at the sawmill is a familiar sight in Canada, some efforts both there and elsewhere are made to utilize it. Similarly vegetable fuel is a by-product in cane-sugar mills. In special circumstances considerable use may be made of other fuels of vegetable origin—industrial alcohol from potatoes and certain oils.

India and Pakistan are almost unique in the very extensive use of hand-made sun-dried cow-dung cakes as a principal fuel in domestic cooking. The serious loss of valuable nitrogenous manure has often been decried; it has been estimated that this source of fuel in India alone is equivalent to 40,000,000 tons of coal per annum, or 32 per cent of India's total fuel, against 34 per cent from wood, 28 per cent from coal, 6 per cent from oil and hydro-electricity.

These renewable sources of vegetable and animal fuels are in total of insignificant importance in comparison with the three great mineral fuels, coal (including peat, lignite, brown coal, true coal and anthracite), mineral oil or petroleum and natural gas. There are several points to be emphasized common to all mineral fuels. First their distribution in the rocks of the earth's crust is the result of conditions in past geological eras, usually many millions of years ago, and has nothing to do with present conditions on the earth's surface. Consequently parts of the world which may be uninhabitable because of present-day climatic conditions so far as dependence on cultivation is concerned, may be, and frequently are, rich in their stores of minerals. Secondly, the mineral fuels are capital resources and are obtained by robber economy: once the existing stores are used up there will be no further supplies, no renewals. Modern methods of prospecting are helping to find deposits which Nature had well hidden, but exploitable resources are far from limitless. Thirdly, world supplies, notably of oil, are often far from regions where the fuel is needed, which raises many questions of transport of a highly specialized nature. Fourthly, the countries which have great reserves are often poverty-stricken in other resources—in fact they include in many cases 'under-developed' countries, whereas it is the great industrialized nations which are ever hungry for these sources of power.

The exhaustible character of mineral fuels has been emphasized on many occasions, notably at the World Power Conference in 1955, but is overshadowed at the present time by the continued new discoveries of oilfields and, to a less extent, of coal reserves. Nevertheless the long-term view is towards new sources of power, particularly from renewable resources.

The force of falling or moving water has been used from time im-

THE BALANCE OF POWER

memorial but its direct use has become unimportant all over the world —as witness the abandoned water-mills of the Scottish crofts, the forgotten hammer ponds of the English Weald or the Sheffield Don-Wharfe valleys. Many a town in New and Old worlds alike owes its original foundation to the presence of a waterfall which on the one hand supplied power for a mill and on the other marked the upstream limit of navigation. Where suitable, the site is now used for the generation of hydro-electric power, but often the falls have reverted to a scenic amenity and little more. But water-power or rather hydro-electric power is of steadily increasing importance. First it is permanently renewed year by year as surely as rains fall and maintain river-flow. But there are difficulties. Since, broadly speaking, electricity cannot be stored, the importance of a source of water-power is linked with low water or minimum flow rather than maximum. This difficulty is normally overcome by storage works to maintain a constant head and flow—hence high initial costs. Another difficulty is that of freezing in countries where winters are cold; excessive losses of water by evaporation are problems in hot lands.

Despite many projected schemes little use has been made in modern times of the tidal movement of ocean waters.

From time to time efforts are made to resuscitate the use of wind power. Windmills are sometimes kept in commission as an insurance against electric power failure—as in parts of Holland in operating the all-important pumps for the polders. Where a main electricity supply is not available, generation by windmills is useful in areas where winds blow constantly but one usually finds them abandoned when a more regular supply becomes available.

It is perhaps surprising that more use is not made of the sun's energy, especially in arid lands with a large proportion of possible sunshine. A simple system of house heating and domestic hot-water supply is now commonly used in the new settlements in Israel; in the East a simple cooking stove based on the principle of concentrating the sun's rays through a glass has been devised and has a modest use. But one sometimes needs to cook when the sun is not shining!

Faith in controlled nuclear fission is now being shown by the construction of atomic power stations. In Britain Calder Hall on the coast of Cumberland first made its contribution to the National Electricity grid in 1957. Subsequently a chain of nuclear power stations was planned. Of necessity they are sited near the coasts or tidal water because of the need of much water for cooling and a certain discharge of possible radioactive effluent. Atomic power is associated in the public mind with the destructive force of atom bombs and partly for this reason, though it is claimed that there is no danger to be associated with atomic power stations, they are being sited away from populous centres.

The Present Position

The present position is that the three main sources of power are coal, oil and water power. We sometimes refer to electricity, gas or petrol as if they were the actual sources of power, forgetting that electricity must be generated by the consumption of coal or oil or by the utilization of water power, whilst coke, gas and petrol are examples of secondary fuels by which coal and oil may be more effectively used.

Where alternative sources of power are available there are some marked contrasts in handling. The bulk and weight of coal required in the majority of manufacturing industries is large in comparison with the bulk and weight of other raw materials. This is not always true—as with the manufacture of pig iron and steel from low-grade iron ores—but it did lead to the concentration of industrial developments on the coal-fields, a phenomenon well seen in such countries as Britain where the Industrial Revolution came before the days of oil or electricity. Coal being a solid must be distributed mainly by rail or water.

By way of contrast oil can be transported large distances by pipeline but overseas movement has involved building of large numbers of tankers, including now some of the largest vessels afloat. Unless suitable on other grounds oilfields have not become industrial regions; on the contrary the oil industry is marked by a certain amount of smell and an element of danger, hence the siting of refineries at a distance from population centres. It is not always realized that the owners of pipelines can handle the oil of different customers, sending it through at different periods. Natural gas can also be transported large distances by pipe. Early in 1959 Britain received the first ship cargo of natural gas—liquified for the purpose of transport.

In the transmission of electricity there are limiting distances related both to capital cost of power lines and also to costs of transmission. In general terms 300 miles is commonly quoted as an approximate economic limit for transmission whether the generation is by coal, oil or water power. This places a restriction particularly on the utilization of water power in remote areas and is marked by a recent tendency for large-scale industry to move to the source of power or reasonably near it—as with the aluminium industry of British Columbia in western Canada.

In his interesting book entitled *Energy in the Future*, Palmer C. Putnam, Consultant to the United States Atomic Energy Commission, makes an elaborate analysis of the whole power position and brings out a number of striking points. Writing in 1952–53 he notes the enormously rapid increase in the consumption of energy with the growth of industrialization and 'high living'. 'In the United States, one-half of all the coal ever consumed has been burned since 1920, and nearly one-half of all the oil and gas ever consumed has been burned since 1940.' Yet it was not until 1890 that coal passed wood as a source of energy in the United States, and in 1952 wood was still five times as important as water power. Taking the world as a whole he estimates that in 1950 the contribution to the world energy system were in the following proportions:

Capital Energy	All coals	55	per cent
	Oil and natural gas	25	per cent
Income Energy	Fuel wood	4	per cent
	Farm wastes	15	per cent
	Falling water	0·7	per cent

Putnam goes on to say: 'There is more coal, oil and gas in the earth's crust than will ever be used. It is not a question of emptying the bin. It is only a question of deciding at what point it no longer pays to dig deeper.'

Coal

Coal, though almost universally used, is not by any means universal in its occurrence. Coal seams vary from a mere fraction of an inch to 100 or more feet in thickness, though it is customary to ignore seams of less than 1½ feet as impossible to exploit economically. The most numerous seams worked are of the order of 3, 4 or 6 feet in thickness, for the costs of working seams much thicker than 6 feet increase rapidly. Seams are usually constant in thickness over wide areas, so that when a coalfield is explored by means of drill holes it is possible to calculate within a relatively small margin of error the total amount of coal actually available. The famous calculations carried out by a Commission of the International Geological Congress of 1913 gave for the first time estimates of the world's coal resources. Naturally the estimates have been modified in many particulars since that date. Table XXII shows some recent figures. In addition to the production of coal and anthracite shown in the tables, there was an output in 1955–57 of an average of over 550,000,000 metric tons of lignite annually. This is mainly important in countries where true coal is scarce; lignite is highly significant in East Germany (over 200 million tons), West Germany (100 million tons), Czechoslovakia and parts of the U.S.S.R.

TABLE XXI

WORLD PRODUCTION OF ANTHRACITE 1943–49 AND 1957

	Millions of metric tons	
	1943–49	1957
China (estimated)	1·0	5·0
France (estimated)	8·0	8·0
French Indo-China (Vietnam)	0·4	1·1
Italy	0·1	0·1
Korea (estimated)	2·5	2·4
Morocco	0·2	0·5
Portugal	0·4	0·5
Spain	1·4	2·8
Britain	3·7	3·4
United States (Pennsylvania)	51·0	22·6
World (estimated)	118·0	

TABLE XXII
Estimated World Resources and Production of Bituminous Coal

	Millions of metric tons			
	Reserves	Production		
	1937[1]	1937[2]	1948[1]	1957
North America:				
Canada	373,000	12	15	10
Mexico	3,000	1	1	1
United States	2,237,000	449	541	438
South America:				
Brazil	5,000	1	2	2
Chile	500	2	2	2
Colombia	27,000	—	1	3
Europe:				
Belgium	11,000	30	27	29
Czechoslovakia	31,000	29	18	24
France	14,000	45	43	48
Germany	369,000	271[3]	91	136
Hungary	500	4	1	2
Italy	500	1	1	1
Netherlands	7,000	14	11	11
Poland	76,000	—	70	93
Saar			13	16
Spain	14,000	7	11	11
U.S.S.R.	1,739,000	118	201	322
United Kingdom	307,000	244	212	220
Asia:				
China	263,000	39	—	125
India	26,000	26	31	44
Japan	22,000	42	34	49
Korea	6,000	?	2	—
Turkey	2,000	2	3	6
Africa:				
Nigeria	3,000	—	0·6	1
Southern Rhodesia	4,000	1	2	4
Union of South Africa	216,000	16	24	34
Oceania:				
Australia	17,000	14	15	18
New Zealand	2,000	2	3	3
World Total	5,697,000	1,384[4]	1,460[5]	1,550

[1] From *Energy Resources of the World*, U.S. Government, 1949.
[2] From *Minerals Yearbook, 1948*, Washington, 1950.
[3] Including Poland.   [5] Includes lignite expressed as coal equivalent.
[4] Figures for lignite not included; anthracite in U.S. not included.

The above figures show that the United States has nearly 40 per cent of known world reserves; Russia, more than 30 per cent; Britain, Germany and Canada each between 5 and 7 per cent. No country in the tropics has as much as 1 per cent.

TABLE XXIII
Estimated World Resources and Production of Crude Petroleum

		\multicolumn{5}{c}{Millions of metric tons}
		Reserves	\multicolumn{4}{c}{Production}
		End of 1958[1]	1947		1958	
				Per cent of world		Per cent of world
North America:	Canada	570	1·1	0·3	21·7	2·4
	Mexico	360	8·0	1·9	13·2	1·5
	United States	4,700	265·1	61·4	327·5	36·3
South America:	Argentina	140	3·1	0·7	4·9	0·5
	Brazil	36	—	—	2·4	0·3
	Colombia	100	3·7	0·9	6·6	0·7
	Ecuador	4	0·1	—	0·4	—
	Peru	46	1·9	0·4	2·6	0·3
	Trinidad	60	3·0	0·7	5·1	0·6
	Venezuela	2,400	62·1	14·4	138·0	15·3
Europe:	Albania	3	0·3	0·1	0·6	0·1
	Austria	43	0·9	0·2	2·9	0·3
	Germany	60	0·6	0·1	4·4	0·5
	Hungary	21	0·6	0·1	0·8	0·1
	Italy	40	—	—	1·5	0·2
	Netherlands	30	0·1	—	1·6	0·2
	Poland	3	0·1	—	0·2	—
	Roumania	140	4·1	1·0	11·5	1·3
	U.S.S.R.	3,700	26·7	6·2	113·5	12·5
Asia:	Bahrain	33	1·3	0·3	2·0	0·2
	British Borneo	70	1·9	0·4	5·1	0·6
	Burma	6	0·1	—	0·5	0·1
	China	70	—	—	2·2	0·2
	India	70	0·3	0·1	0·4	—
	Indonesia	1,200	1·1	0·3	16·8	1·9
	Iran	4,700	22·1	5·1	41·0	4·5
	Iraq	3,600	5·1	1·2	35·8	4·0
	Japan	9	0·1	—	0·4	—
	Kuwait	8,600	2·3	0·5	70·1	7·8
	Kuwait Neutral	6,860	—	—	4·0	0·4
	Saudi Arabia	7,200	12·9	3·0	50·4	5·6
Africa:	Egypt	60	1·3	0·3	3·0	0·3
	Sahara	520	—	—	0·9	0·1
WORLD TOTAL		39,400	431·5	100·0	905·2	100·0
Free world:	Western Hemisphere				523·8	57·8
	Eastern Hemisphere				252·4	27·9
U.S.S.R., China and allies					129·2	14·3

[1] Proven Reserves according to *Oil and Gas Journal*

In 1960 and 1961 there was a huge increase in production from the Sahara (especially Algeria).

THE BALANCE OF POWER

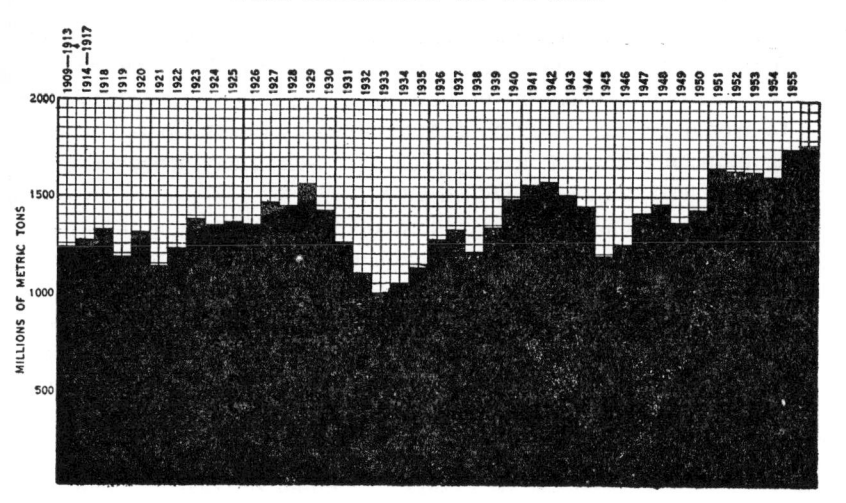

Fig. 30
The World Production of Coal

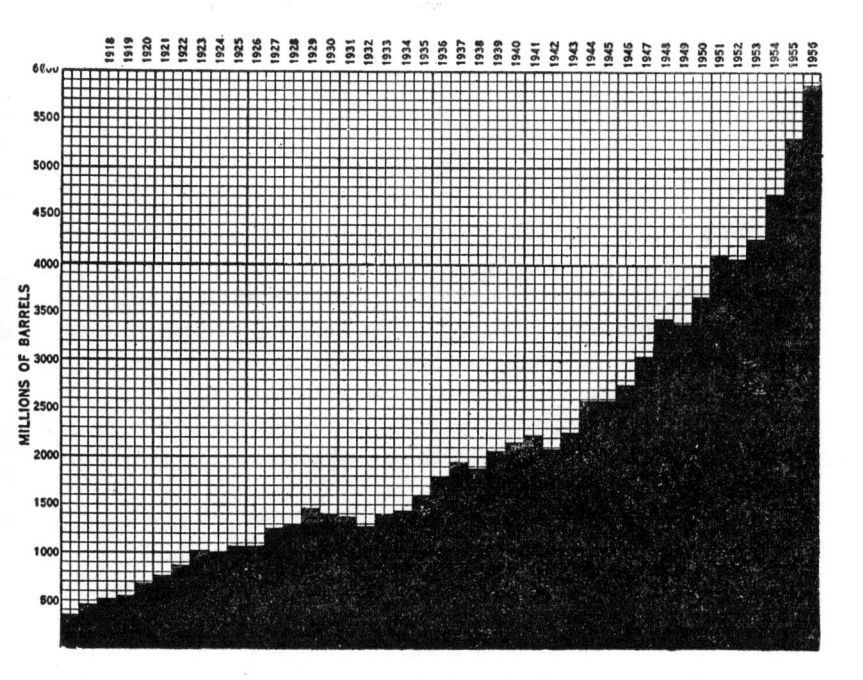

Fig. 31
The World Production of Oil

THE BALANCE OF POWER

A large proportion of the coal mined is not burnt as such. In Britain, for example, about one-eighth goes to coke ovens and even more to gas works. An ever-increasing proportion—rising from 4 per cent in 1923 to over 20 per cent by 1955—goes to electricity works. Coal-gas can be sent considerable distances by pipe; carbo-electricity generated at or near pithead can be widely distributed.

With a generally rising standard of living coal-mining, even with extensive mechanized extraction and haulage, had tended to become an increasingly unattractive occupation. Labour must be attracted to the industry by high wages: soon the costs of production combined with heavy distributive costs place oil in a favourable competitive position. The fall in coal output in the United States is evidence of this: even a country like Britain, with abundant coal and no oil, tends to rely more and more on imported oils.

Attempts to eliminate the drudgery of mining have resulted in a considerable development (5 per cent of output) of open-cast coal in Britain. The hydrogenation of coal, whereby it is converted to oil by combination with hydrogen under high pressure, has been virtually abandoned owing to high costs: the gasification of coal underground without mining has not so far proved very successful.

Mineral Oil

Mineral oil or petroleum, like coal derived from organic remains of past geological periods, is also found in the sedimentary rocks. Quite probably it originated as small globules scattered through beds of sand, but in the course of time the globules collected and so we have the phenomenon of oil pools, trapped by a rock structure that prevents escape of the oil to the surface to be dissipated and lost. The task of the oil geologist is to locate the hidden oil pools from the disposition of the rocks and such indications as seepages, which are in fact the escapes of small quantities to the surface.

Two important considerations about oilfields are that each field represents the accumulated resources from a wide surrounding area and, secondly, that it is impossible to calculate reserves with anything like the accuracy possible for coal. The maintenance of the world's output of oil is dependent on the continued discovery of new fields, and although the pessimists of two or three decades ago have been constantly confounded by new discoveries, we cannot escape the fact that the world

THE BALANCE OF POWER

demand for oil is still rising and that reserves are likely to be exhausted long before many of the major reserves of coal have been touched. We can go so far as to say that the possession of oil is thus a temporary asset, however valuable. It has, of course, a great advantage over coal in ease of handling through pipeline and by tanker and in convenience of storage. World demand for oil is still rising. However, recent discoveries have more than kept pace: for example in 1958 Canada had become worried trying to find markets for increasing production from the Prairie Provinces, and experts claim that known reserves have outstripped even the rapid rise in production. Because of the high cost of mining oil shale and of obtaining the oil from the shale, vast reserves in many parts of the world have at present little economic importance.

The graph attached of world oil production (Fig. 31) shows how rapid has been the rise in total output. Table XXIII illustrates how quickly new producers have altered the world picture.

Fuel and Power in the Under-developed Lands

In preceding chapters stress has been laid on the supreme necessity of securing adequate food for the peoples of the world. It is idle to pretend that development could, or should, stop at that one objective. Even the simple end of an adequate and a sufficiently varied diet cannot be achieved without fuel for cooking. Very quickly development comes to include a decent standard of housing—adequate heating and lighting, water-supply, and sanitation. We of the Western world have witnessed a world evolving from a coal age, through a gas age, to the day when a public supply of electric energy is almost regarded as part of the individual's birthright. In the under-developed areas it must be a plunge straight into the electric age. The touch of a switch which means a good cheap light, a motor in action for a thousand jobs (not the least being the pumping of a supply of good water), the control through electric refrigeration over the preservation of nearly all types of food—these must be a primary aim of development even if crude fuels continue to be used for cooking and heating.

What, then, are the resources of fuel and power in the under-developed lands?

Table XXII of the world's coal resources and coal production shows concentration in a few areas. In the New World, the vast resources and output of coal in the United States and, to a lesser degree, in Canada

THE BALANCE OF POWER

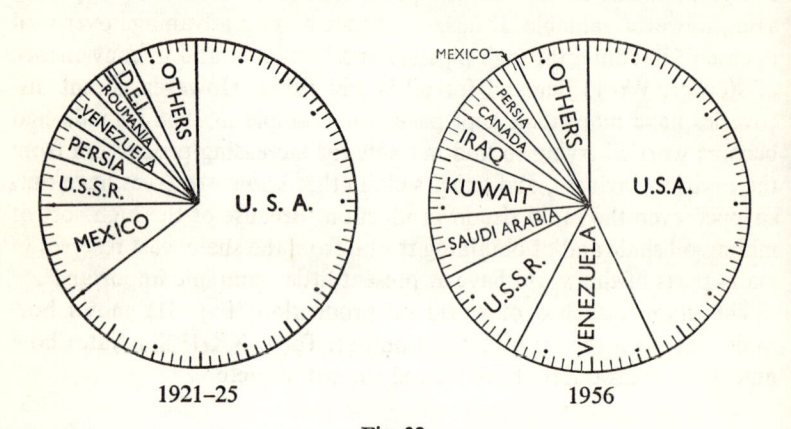

Fig. 32

The World's Oil Producers

[Pie chart 1921–25: U.S.A., MEXICO, U.S.S.R., PERSIA, VENEZUELA, ROUMANIA, D.E.I., OTHERS]

[Pie chart 1956: U.S.A., VENEZUELA, U.S.S.R., SAUDI ARABIA, KUWAIT, IRAQ, CANADA, PERSIA, MEXICO, OTHERS]

contrast with the poverty of the whole of Latin America. Naturally one asks the question, how far is this just lack of knowledge—that deposits have not yet been located? For reasons related to geological structure which will be considered later, we may regard Latin America's poverty in coal as a proven fact—it is unlikely that any sizeable undiscovered fields exist.

The distribution of coal in the Eastern Hemisphere is equally irregular. In Europe there is the belt of rich fields stretching from Britain, through northern France, Belgium, Holland, Germany, Poland and Czechoslovakia into Russia and a few fields outside, as in northern Spain, but little elsewhere. There is no doubt that the U.S.S.R. both in Europe and Asia has vast coalfields; China's reserves, though much less extensive than once believed, are large, and so are India's. Japan is less fortunate; with the exception of Turkey, other Asiatic countries also have but little coal. Australia has at least one really large field of good coal and others of economic importance. In Africa a large and valuable field exists in the Union of South Africa and some good coal in Rhodesia, but over the vast stretches of under-developed tropical Africa there is little or no coal, even allowing for the Nigerian deposits and

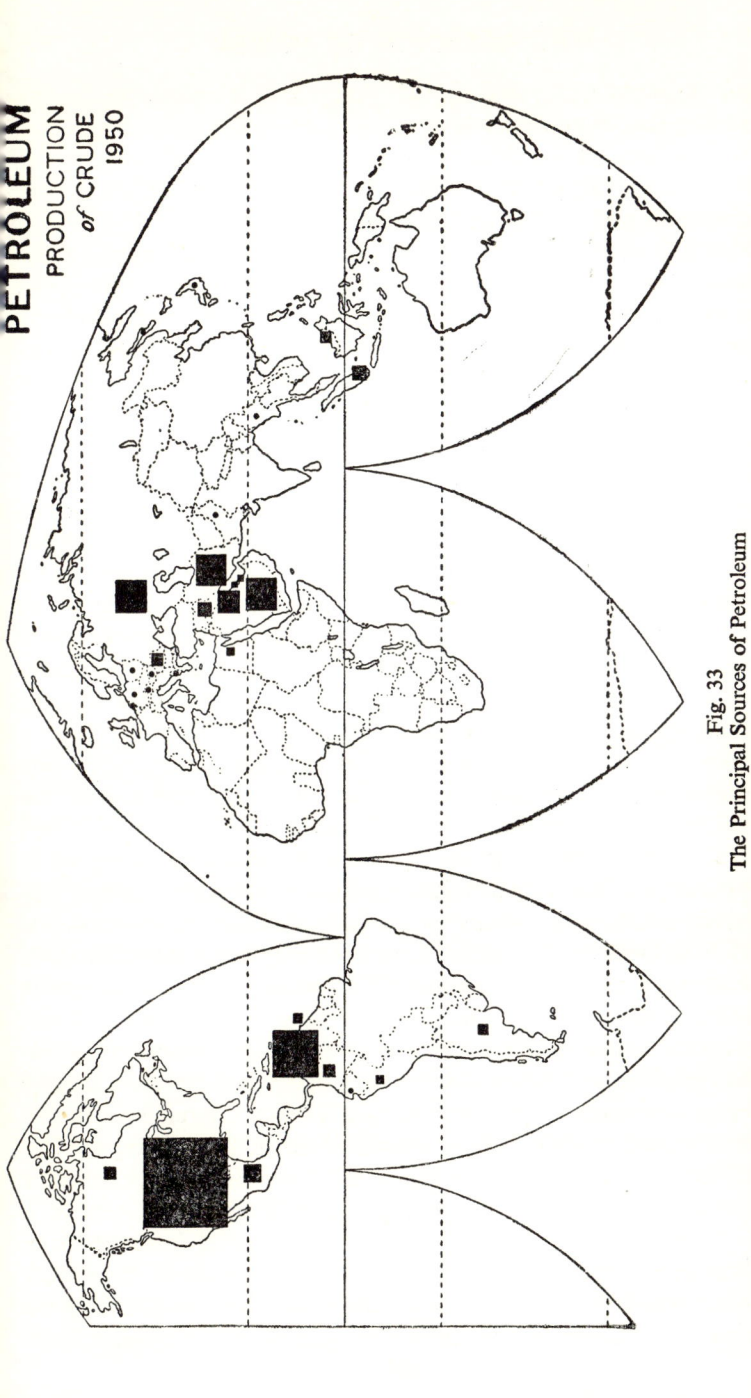

Fig. 33
The Principal Sources of Petroleum
To this map should now be added the very large production from the Sahara (Algeria and Libya) and the more modest production of Nigeria and Gabun.

THE BALANCE OF POWER

others in Sierra Leone and Tanganyika, which are moderate-quality lignites or sub-bituminous coals.

If, therefore, we are thinking of the under-developed areas in the world as those lying primarily within the tropics, coal is unlikely to play a substantial part in their development.

With petroleum the position is somewhat different. The great oilfields of South America have brought wealth and rapid change to Venezuela, Colombia, Ecuador and Peru; and they have projected the limelight on to Bolivia and Paraguay. In the Old World oil discoveries and exploitations in Iran, Iraq, Arabia and the coast-lands of the Persian Gulf, parts of the East Indies, and to a less extent central Burma have brought about extensive economic development.

It is only eight years since I wrote: '... it becomes increasingly doubtful whether petroleum will ever play a large part in the development of tropical Africa'. The discoveries since then are evidence of the surprises still possible. The small fields on the Suez Gulf coast of Egypt, and a few small wells in Morocco were then almost the only oil in the whole continent. Now other Egyptian fields have been developed on the coasts of Sinai, Nigeria has an output from fields near the coast, but the really significant developments are those in the heart of the Sahara on both sides of the Libyan–southern Algeria border.

If we turn to water as a source of power, we are turning to one inevitably destined to play a major part in the development of the humid tropics. It is in the lands which today we call under-developed that the greatest resources lie—in South America and above all in tropical Africa. The very fact that Africa is a vast plateau means that the rivers meandering over its surface must find their way over rapids and falls to lower levels, that they have frequently entrenched themselves in deep gorges providing ideal dam sites. Further, if artificial reservoirs must be created, there are often vast areas sparsely settled where flooding is not a serious problem. Often there can be and should be a combined irrigation and power development. Early in the present century when an adventurous young man named Winston Churchill penetrated to the almost untrodden heart of Africa where the Nile leaving the vast Lake Victoria plunged over the Ripon and Owen Falls, he recognized a power site unsurpassed in its potential. Today towns and villages over a wide radius, as well as modern factories, are supplied from the Owen Falls power scheme. In the Katanga are many power works: the mighty Zambezi below the famed Victoria Falls is now harnessed in the great Kariba Dam, completed in 1959 only just over a 100 years since

THE BALANCE OF POWER

Livingstone discovered the Falls in the heart of the erstwhile Darkest Africa. In the west, Ghana has the huge Volta Dam project already part completed.

Nothing is deserving of closer study than water resources—and it is far more than a question of hydro-electricity, important as that may be. As I have already stated, I believe that the control of water is the key to development in tropical lands.

IX

MINERALS

The resources of farm and forest, in common with those of running water, are renewable resources. Properly treated land will go on yielding food and raw materials in perpetuity. In sharp contrast nearly all mineral resources are capital resources: once used up they are not renewed. Man's main interest is in the stores of those minerals which, because of their proved value to him, are denoted 'economic minerals'. Many deposits are deeply buried; many are difficult to locate; some are of great extent; others exist in small quantities, are superficial, and quickly exhausted. Man's first task is to find the deposits, then to work them until exhaustion of the resource puts an end to the enterprise and the associated settlement has to be abandoned or alternative occupations found for its inhabitants. Thus minerals are capital resources won by what is often called 'robber' economy.

Renewable and Capital Resources

To some extent, then, it must always be true that mineral resources are a temporary rather than a permanent asset to a country. But this generalization needs qualification. The reserves of certain minerals are so vast that there is little or no possibility of their being exhausted in the foreseeable future. The natural reserves of limestone would seem to assure an ample supply of lime for cement in most countries; and it is doubtful whether any important country is likely to exhaust its reserves of brick-making materials. Many of the known reserves of coal may be expected to last for hundreds, indeed thousands, of years.

There is still an element of luck associated with exploration for minerals. Even if the romantic days of the gold rush are past, there is still the hope that the amateur armed with a geiger counter may detect some hitherto unsuspected uranium-ore body. Since there may be no

MINERALS

surface trace of either a great oil deposit or a great mass of ore, there are still those who, with so great a prize, will risk a wildcat well or an experimental boring. Within the last quarter-century, however, geophysical methods of detecting what lies hidden below the surface, often masked by superficial deposits, have become increasingly important, though the final test rests with the drill.

Also increasing technical skill renders of value mineral deposits considered worthless in the past. Since an 'ore' is technically a deposit from which one or more metals may be profitably extracted, what is not considered an ore one year may become one the next. Old dumps are constantly being worked over for the more effective extraction of gold, silver, or other metals. New smelting processes are permitting the reduction of heretofore unused ores, as copper sulphides at Chuquicamata, Chile. The factor of location also enters in. A good many years ago when I first went to Burma to prospect for oil in the Chindwin River basin, I was very much excited at finding a hill which seemed to be a solid mass of iron ore. I had no means of testing even specific gravity, but did my best by makeshift means—it was obviously not high grade, but still, what a discovery! I rode back two days' journey to the nearest telegraph, sent cables to secure a prospecting monopoly, and advised my head office in Rangoon of my action. The reply from headquarters came quickly. It read: 'What on earth do you think is the good of iron ore in the Chindwin stop get on with your work.' Thus I learned that accessibility is a factor of great importance in assessing the value of an ore deposit. Had, of course, the ore body been of such size or richness as to outweigh disadvantages of location the position would have been quite different. This is well seen in the recent opening up of the huge iron ore deposits of northern Quebec and the Labrador interior—sufficiently rich and extensive to warrant the construction of a 400-mile railway into barren country of extreme climate. On the other hand the extensive brown coal deposits known to occur over large areas in the Antarctic continent are unlikely to prove sufficiently valuable as to attract development.

Finally, there is the enormously significant fact that man is constantly finding new needs for materials previously counted of little or no value. We need scarcely remind ourselves of the sudden importance assumed by ores of radium, and the present importance of uranium ores and other fissionable material used in atomic work. It is not long since aluminium was so difficult to extract from its ores as to be a rare and expensive metal, and the value of magnesium in making light alloys was

MINERALS

still unknown. On the tin-fields of Malaya the separation of the tin ore from the then useless wolframite was a costly process. With the development of tungsten steels and filaments there came the sudden demand for what had previously been a waste product. Within the present century cadmium, selenium, tantalum, zirconium and other metals have been transformed from curiosities in the chemist's laboratory to substances of commercial importance.

Geological Structure and Mineral Deposits

Water power depends on the circumstances of precipitation as well as on the form of the ground. Generally, as far as other mineral resources are concerned, no such direct relationship exists as that between water power and climate. Like all generalized statements this needs some qualification. In the more arid parts of the world, where salts are derived from deposits at or near the surface, as the sodium nitrate of Chile, or from salt lakes such as the Dead Sea, they may be said to owe their existence to the aridity of the climate. But such cases do not render invalid the broad general statement that mineral deposits depend on geological structure and not on climate.

The geological structure of any part of the earth's surface is the result of many millions of years of the earth's evolution. It is something fixed and definite; the mineral resources of any country are an endowment provided by Nature not to be changed or varied by man. The use which a country may make of its mineral deposits will, of course, depend on many factors, notably the country's resources in men, materials, and money. But whatever the stage of development, the fact remains that the mineral resources are there or are not there, as the case may be. The possession of minerals to some extent redresses the balance between nations, and some that are unfortunate in their climatic conditions are fortunate in their mineral resources.

Present and Future Mineral Production

Minerals, it might be said, have provided the world with that element of chance that appeals to the gambling instinct in mankind. Whereas the production of food and other agricultural raw materials results in a settled or slowly changing pattern of farms, villages and towns, the

MINERALS

exploitation of minerals results in an unstable pattern of human settlement, sometimes liable to violent and rapid changes. To take a well-known instance, gold was discovered in the remote Yukon in 1895, more than 500 miles from the nearest town on the coast of the Pacific. When the news leaked out, the Gold Rush began. There followed the extraordinary migration of thousands of prospectors to Skagway, up over the Chilkoot Pass, later by the White Pass, to Bennett, and thence by lake and river down the Yukon to Dawson City. Skagway leapt in population from virtually nothing to several thousand in a matter of weeks; Bennett, too. One of the most breath-taking mountain railways in the world was built in a matter of months. When the placer deposits gave out almost as suddenly as they had been developed, Skagway became a ghost town, though it has had several new leases of life, and Bennett reverted to a waste of scrubland, with a derelict wooden church and a railway station; the Gold Rush railway now extracts its gold from the pockets of summer tourists.

There are ghost towns in the western United States, such as Arizona's famed Tombstone, and in Australia, where Bendigo and Ballarat live in public memory more through the stories of Sherlock Holmes than through their former importance as gold producers. And so in many other parts of the world.

We see the same thing happening with oil. But it is more difficult to realize that the same phenomena are being witnessed on the British coalfields. And even in Britain this particular problem has scarcely yet been faced. Coal was worked in the Newcastle area of the Northumbrian and Durham coalfield at least as early as the fourteenth century; in its western part, where the seams reach the surface, the coal has been actively worked for a century and a half and the field is largely exhausted. But over that period there have grown up not only colliery villages, but also towns of considerable size, equipped with public utilities and all the paraphernalia of civic life. Were it not for such substantial developments and the investment that they represent, these towns of the exhausted coalfield would also be ghost towns. The reason for their existence has now disappeared. What of their future? Are they to be allowed to decay and die by inches, or should positive planning step in and, by encouraging new forms of industrial development, revitalize the area? This is a problem common to many of the older industrial areas of Europe which grew up originally on coalfields.

In considering this question we must not confuse the older exhausted or partly exhausted sections of the coalfields with the vigorous life of

MINERALS

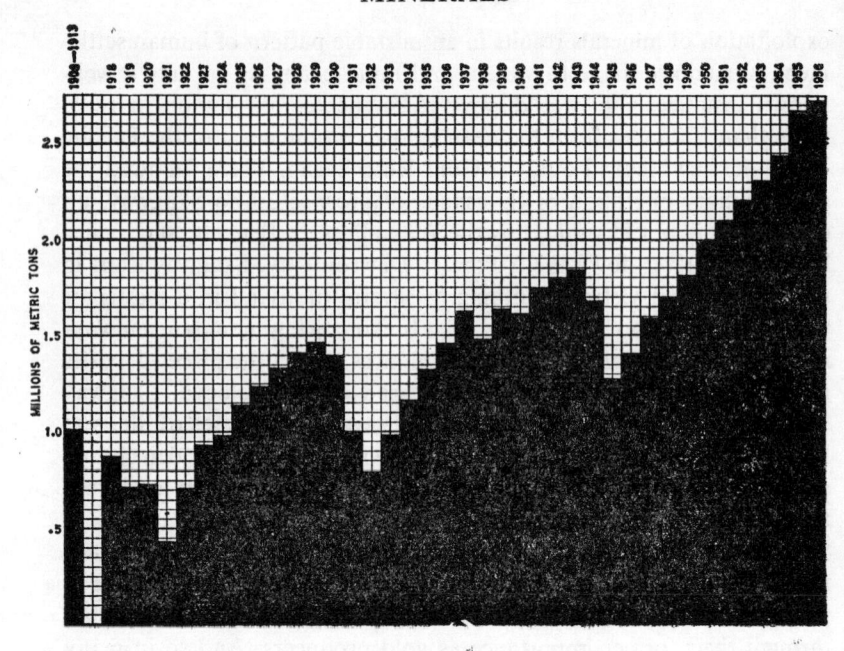

Fig .34

Graph of World Production of Zinc
In contrast to the steady demand for foodstuffs, this graph shows very
clearly the effect of periods of depression

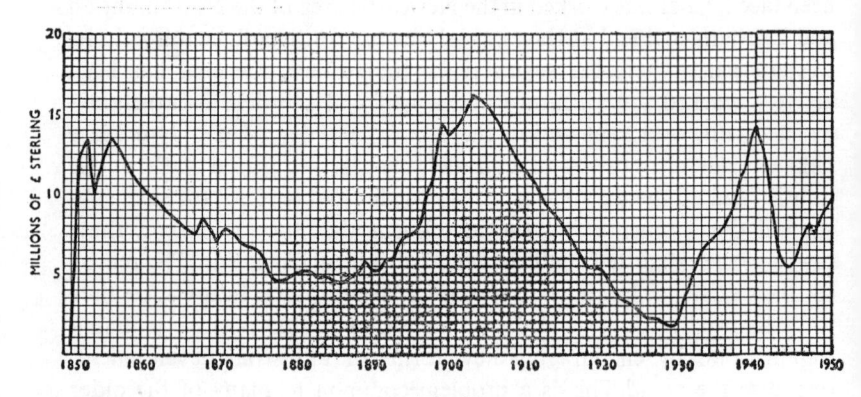

Fig. 35

Graph of Gold Production in Australia

MINERALS

those parts now being actively developed. Many writers, particularly American writers, have fallen into the error of believing that British coal is becoming exhausted. It certainly is not, but it is becoming exhausted in certain of the older parts of the fields.

The phenomena of discovery, development, decay, death, universally characteristic of mineral deposits and mining settlements, are evident all over the world. Graphs of mineral production, particularly of the metalliferous minerals which occur in veins liable to peter out and disappear in depth, show wide fluctuations. People do not eat minerals. Whereas the demand for food is relatively stable, minerals yielding material for the manufacture of capital equipment or consumer goods are liable to be affected much more by periods of depression and suffer much more from price fluctuations. In times of prosperity, mining is active; in times of depression, mines close down. This is another reason why mining communities are unstable. Any economic geographer knows how difficult it is to keep up to date when one is discussing mineral resources and mineral production of a particular country. What is a true statement today may be false tomorrow. What is rightly described one year as the largest gold mine in the whole North American continent may be flooded and abandoned within twelve months—as actually happened at Juneau. It is almost impossible to talk in specific terms about the potential production of minerals. What we do know, however, is that immense possibilities still exist in the world, in geologically unexplored ancient rocks of Brazil and Africa, for instance. In some cases it may be that superficial deposits render the task of discovery difficult by hiding with a thick blanket what lies underneath. In other cases it is the remoteness of unexplored areas, such as the heart of Brazil, or the far north of Canada, which has prevented mineral discovery and development.

It was no fault of the early prospectors, usually without maps and armed only with primitive equipment, that they failed to find deposits which can now be detected by new methods. Outline geological maps can be prepared from air photographs, even before the area is visited by a ground party; geophysical methods including prospecting from the air permit detection of ore bodies even deeply buried.

There is no doubt that many countries at present regarded as unimportant are destined to leap into world-wide significance as their mineral resources become known.

MINERALS

The International Role of Mining

This leads to a consideration of the way in which minerals may redress the balance between nations. In so far as a country lies within a certain type of climate, its agricultural development must take place along certain lines, and its potential production can in many respects be calculated or forecast. Similarly by virtue of the climate and the build or relief of the country the areas capable of cultivation, of afforestation, of being developed for water power, are either known or can be readily surveyed. Minerals and mining provide the unknown quantities and may give us the surprises of the future. Even countries which have long had detailed geological and mineralogical surveys are found to have unexpected resources. During World War II borings for oil in Yorkshire revealed deposits of potassium and other salts which, though not at present exploitable, may be valuable in the future, and were certainly unsuspected previously. It may even be that whereas countries are left to work out their own salvation in the matter of feeding themselves, international trade must continue so long as their minerals are essential in our modern existence. I shall discuss later the remarkable trend so evident in the United States for the finding of substitutes for most things in life, and it may be urged that where we now regard certain metals as of vital importance, substitutes may be found in the future. Yet it is difficult to see how minerals can be robbed entirely of their great international role.

This role is an ancient one. Throughout history minerals have played a decisive part not only in the rise and fall of great powers, but in the successive development of previously under-developed areas. Salt was one of the earliest minerals both to promote international trade and to provoke wars. To this day the word 'salary' reminds us that it referred originally to money paid to a Roman soldier to buy the all-important *sal* (salt).

It would seem that the earliest of the traders to come from the continent of Europe to the shores of the British Isles came in order to secure some of the gold ornaments then made from the long-since exhausted gold deposits of North Wales and Ireland. For many centuries before Christ the trade of the Mediterranean, the heart of the known world, was dominated by Cretan and Phoenician metal merchants who shipped copper from Cyprus, gold, silver and copper from Spain, and later tin from Cornwall in Britain. It was the silver from Spain which enabled Carthage to hire mercenaries to fight the Romans. When Carthage was driven from Spain by the Romans it was the possession of these mineral spoils that enabled Rome to become the great world power of the day. She secured gold, silver, copper and iron from Spain; invaded and conquered Britain for lead and silver and copper and tin; and subdued Greece for more silver and copper. Historians ascribe the decline and fall of the Roman Empire to various causes; some see it in the over-development of the civil service; some trace it to the dwindling supplies of metals.

Be that as it may, the story has been repeated many times since. The discovery of the New World itself by Columbus was part of the quest for the gold, precious stones, and other treasures of the Indies and the incredible half-century of Spanish conquest that followed was dictated essentially by the lust of the *conquistadores* for gold and silver. Sea power passed to Britain when her ships seized the treasure-laden Spanish galleons on the high seas and shortly after defeated the Armada.

With the coming of the Industrial Revolution it was England's possession of large deposits of coal suitable for coking and of iron ore and limestone flux in close proximity that laid the foundation of her world leadership in the nineteenth century.

The last century has but quickened the pace. Gold accidentally discovered in California in 1848 led to the rush of '49 and so to the opening up and settlement of the almost unknown western half of the continent. In 1851 the discovery of gold in Australia (see Fig. 35) led to the migration of more than a million Britishers to what had been previously a despised 'convict settlement'. In 1867 the discovery of diamonds at Kimberley and a few years later of the world's richest goldfield on the Rand led not only to the development of South Africa but really to the whole opening up of Africa and to the scramble for African territory by Britain, France, Belgium and Germany. Copper brought both railway and settlers to the Belgian and Rhodesian Katanga. Rhodesia, named after the British pioneer Cecil John Rhodes, was itself explored and established by profits from mining in South Africa.

In the present century it is the liquid gold, petroleum, that has come to the fore as a factor in economic and political development. The discovery of the oilfields of the Maracaibo Basin has caused profound changes in the economic life of Venezuela. It was not the possibility of food production in the Chaco which underlay the boundary dispute between Bolivia and Paraguay and led to the war of 1933–34, but the possibility of oil. The search for oil actuated the exploration of little-

MINERALS

known Borneo and New Guinea. Perhaps the most staggering modern development of all is the sudden transformation of the poverty-stricken sheikdoms of the Persian Gulf to positions of worldly affluence and international significance—all since 1932 when oil was struck in Bahrain Island, with the geologists still living who had reported the area worthless.

Within the past few years the whole of Canada's economy has been profoundly changed by new mineral discoveries—the rich oil and gas fields of Alberta and Saskatchewan, the iron ores of Ungava and northern Quebec, the gold, radium and uranium deposits of the far north in the Great Bear Lake and Great Slave Lake areas. In 1948 Canada imported 33,000,000 barrels of oil from the United States; by 1957 there was a home production of 182,000,000 barrels worth $445,000,000; in 1948 uranium ore was unnamed among minerals produced, by 1958 it was third in order of value at $225,000,000.

All this affords justification for the statement that minerals still provide a main incentive for man's interest in under-developed lands; still provide the surprise element; still underlie national stability and development; still involve international rivalry and, whether we like it or not, exploitation by the strong.

Even the largest of the world's political units cannot claim to be self-sufficient in the full range of minerals and metals required in our modern civilization. Probably the U.S.S.R. approaches most nearly to self-sufficiency; on the other hand the United States, despite an overwhelmingly strong position in many directions, lacks certain essential mineral commodities and is rapidly exhausting her known reserves of others. This was in part the theme of Dr. Isaiah Bowman's survey, 'The Geographical Situation of the United States in Relation to World Policies', presented before the Royal Geographical Society in 1948.

Minerals and Under-developed Areas

It is instructive to review the world sources of some of the leading metals. Thereby is emphasized the dependence of the great powers on otherwise under-developed areas. It may be that certain under-developed areas will be able to pay for their own development. As Sir Frank Stockdale pointed out in a survey of British Colonial developments shortly before his sudden death, 'most mining developments have taken place at the instance of private enterprise'. The interest of governments is a comparatively new development.

Aluminium, as the oxide alumina, is a constituent of all clays and one

BAUXITE 1957

Fig. 36
Chief Sources of
Bauxite

Pie chart sections: U.S.A., U.S.S.R., JAMAICA, DUTCH GUIANA, BRITISH GUIANA, W. AFRICA, MALAYA, OTHERS. Shaded edge labelled LESS DEVELOPED COUNTRIES.

COPPER 1957

Fig. 37
Chief Sources of
Copper

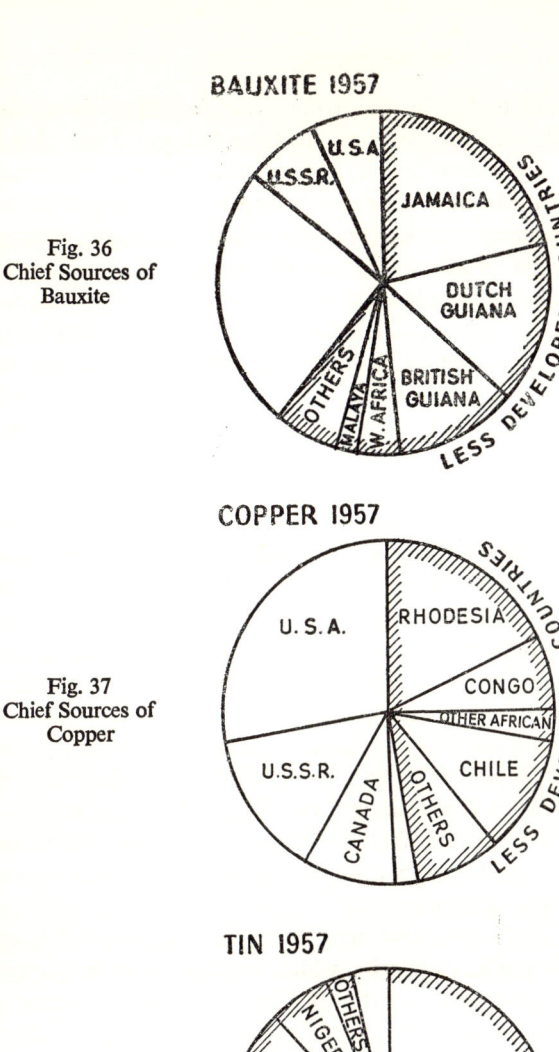

Pie chart sections: U.S.A., RHODESIA, CONGO, OTHER AFRICAN, CHILE, OTHERS, CANADA, U.S.S.R. Shaded edge labelled LESS DEVELOPED COUNTRIES.

TIN 1957

Fig. 38
Chief Sources of
Tin Ore

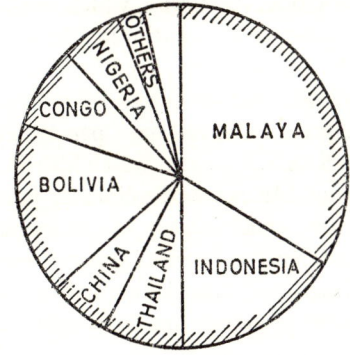

Pie chart sections: MALAYA, INDONESIA, THAILAND, CHINA, BOLIVIA, CONGO, NIGERIA, OTHERS.

In each diagram, the less developed countries are edged with shading

MINERALS

of the most abundant metals in the earth's crust, but the bulk of the product is obtained from the not very common bauxite. Since cheap electric power, usually hydro-electric, is needed for the high temperatures of the reduction furnaces, the ore is brought to the power. In the inter-war years, Germany and Canada (following the United States) were two of the chief producers of aluminium, and they imported almost all the bauxite they needed. Canada derived most of her supply of the ore from British Guiana, which alone produced nearly 2,000,000 tons of the ore; Dutch Guiana (Surinam) overtook British Guiana in 1947 and in that year the two Guianas alone furnished nearly one-half of the world's total supply. Even since then there have been some remarkable changes, notably the exploitation of deposits in Jamaica and West Africa. Thus in 1956 the first three suppliers of bauxite were, in order: Dutch Guiana, Jamaica and British Guiana with over half the world's total. French West Africa, Ghana, Malaya and Indonesia provided another 6 per cent. In the meantime too the great Kitimat power works in British Columbia have been developed for smelting the ore and we have here the perfect example of the less developed tropical lands making a major contribution to the economy of the Western world.[1]

Copper has shown an enormously increased world demand. Ores are widely distributed, and the United States, in the western states, yields more than a quarter of the world's supply (1956); Chile produces about a seventh; and Northern Rhodesia and the Belgian Katanga nearly a fifth. The African field, with its 500,000,000 tons of 4 per cent ore is the largest actual and potential copper belt in the world, and it is in the heart of another under-developed area.

Tin is more localized in its distribution. Nearly all tin is smelted from the heavy and stable oxide, cassiterite, which, washed out of its parent lode, is commonly found as 'stream tin' in alluvial deposits. Practically no tin is found in the United States, and little in Canada and less than 2 per cent of the world's output comes from Europe. Thus the chief users depend entirely on imports. Sixty per cent of the present total (1956), excluding the U.S.S.R., about which little is known, comes from south-east Asia—from Malaya and adjoining parts of Thailand and Lower Burma, and two small islands of Indonesia. Another sixth of world output comes from the heart of Bolivia, important percentages from the Belgian Congo and Nigeria, a small percentage from China. Again the main sources of supply are from otherwise under-developed

[1] But now the remote York peninsula in Queensland is claiming the world's largest deposits.

MINERALS

areas. In all, the countries mentioned supply nearly 95 per cent of the total.

Tungsten is also restricted in its occurrence. In 1913 Burma led world production, followed by the United States and Portugal. World War I stimulated production, and China, Korea and Bolivia were added to the list of producers. The great importance of tungsten in the manufacture of high-tension steels led to an intensive search for new sources of supply during the Second World War, though with limited success. Today the list of substantial producers also includes Brazil and Tasmania.

Other ferro-alloys of importance are nickel-iron and manganese-iron. About 60 per cent of all nickel comes from Canada, 20 per cent from Russia, but 12 per cent from the French Pacific island of New Caledonia. Russia is far in the lead in world output of manganese, followed by India, South Africa, Ghana, Morocco and the Belgian Congo.

Radium is, of course, a rare metal and so are workable ores of uranium, of which it is a disintegration product. The discovery of the radium-uranium ore of Great Bear Lake in Canada's North-West Territories in 1930 well illustrates how a single mineral deposit can completely alter the whole world picture. Once again the vast mineral wealth of the United States has been demonstrated in the lead taken in the output of uranium ores.

Nearly a third of the world's antimony, important in type metal, flame-proofed textiles, and other industrial uses, comes from South Africa. Mexico and Peru are the world's largest producers of bismuth. The leading producers of chrome ore may all be described as among the less developed countries—Turkey, Philippines, South Africa, and Rhodesia—with about two-thirds of the whole.

Practically all the world's cobalt is produced by the Belgian Congo, Northern Rhodesia and Morocco, except for about a quarter from Canada and the United States.

A non-metallic mineral of much interest is asbestos. The bulk of the world's supply comes from eastern Canada, followed by Southern Rhodesia, the Union of South Africa and the little British Protectorate of Swaziland. Africa is *par excellence* the home of the diamond—the Union of South Africa, South-West Africa, the Belgian Congo, Ghana, Tanganyika, Sierra Leone and French West Africa. The spectacular discovery of diamonds in Tanganyika changed considerably the economic position of that territory.

With metals whose ores are more widely distributed we may note the important part played by the remoter regions of the world—the gold of Southern Rhodesia, the Belgian Congo and West Africa, the silver-lead of the Bawdwin mines of Burma, the silver of the Peruvian and Bolivian Andes and the Belgian Congo. The position of iron ore is particularly interesting. Although iron is very widely distributed in the earth's crust, it is only when the content of metallic iron reaches a certain proportion that minerals or rocks become 'iron ore'. Many low-grade iron ores are only worked if they are easily accessible or if the countries concerned have no better supplies. The great European producers have come to rely more and more on imported ores, and once again under-developed areas have or may have an important part to play. For example, iron ore is now shipped from Algeria and Sierra Leone to Britain, and there are large exports from Malaya and Liberia.

The present trend is for governments to take a large part in the work of survey and exploration. The Australian Government pioneered with geophysical reconnaissance surveys, the Canadian Government with the use of air surveys. The British Government set up an Overseas (formerly Colonial) Geological Survey where the small British personnel available is aided by American geologists. The first issue of its bulletin, *Colonial Geology and Mineral Resources*, appeared in 1950. It now publishes annually a valuable *Statistical Summary of the Mineral Industry*.

X

STATUS QUO—LAND AND PEOPLE

Since any planning for the future must start from the present position, it seems obvious in my way of thinking that we should seek both to know and understand the present position, how and why it has arisen. More particularly am I sure that this principle should be applied in the sphere of land use and land planning. We need to know the *status quo* both with regard to land and people. This, I suggest, is the natural viewpoint of a member of one of the older civilizations. As a Britisher, my country is a palimpsest of more than two thousand years of settlement and development. Ancient Britons of many stocks, Romans, Anglo-Saxons, Danes and Norwegians, Normans, wave after wave of political refugees from continental Europe: each have left their mark on my homeland and its people. Nearly two thousand years ago the urban-minded and tidy Romans made some wise decisions in town location, but did not escape the mistakes of the pioneer in some of the country estates they laid out. The land-hungry Anglo-Saxons were country-wise beyond belief in their knowledge of good soils—we have scarcely found any they missed in the succeeding twelve or thirteen centuries—and water-supplies, whilst the parishes and counties they delineated have persisted with little change to the present day. The Normans, building in stone, crystallized for ever the Anglo-Saxon pattern of land use: because it was founded, generally speaking, on sound principles of land use, the landlord-tenant system lived on after the enclosures and still dominates the scene. The major woodlands to survive the greed of medieval timber merchants are the old royal hunting grounds: many of the most valued recreational areas of today are the manorial wastes or commons left unenclosed for the use of otherwise landless peasants. Within the past two centuries over this age-old pattern of rural-agricultural Britain there has spread with increasing impetus the alien pattern of urban-industrial Britain, at first from its coalfield centres, but latterly from areas based on other factors.

STATUS QUO—LAND AND PEOPLE

In its broad essentials a similar story of the evolution of the land use pattern is true of all the older settled countries—embracing most of Europe and much of Asia. There is so much to learn from the past enshrined in the present, so much of frozen history worthy of preservation in the future world that it is unthinkable to ignore either present or past.

In a young country where the story of settlement goes back but a few generations the viewpoint may well be very different. The mistakes of the pioneers may still be readily visible. Flying over the arid lands of southern Nebraska, for example, one traces the monotonous rectangular layout of farms and farm roads—in itself a fundamental mistake, because Nature is never rectangular—only to see the roads fading, disused, into an arid sandy waste with ruined deserted farmsteads still visible where the unlucky ones ventured beyond the pioneer fringe and lost the battle against an uncompromising Nature.

But whether it is to reveal the wisdom or unwisdom of our ancestors a survey of the present position is never a waste of time. A factual survey of present land use was the first object of the Land Utilisation Survey of Britain which I initiated in the nineteen-thirties. We were fortunate in having a complete cover of detailed base maps (on the scale of 1: 10,560 or 6 inches to the mile), though some were seriously out of date and the task of my innumerable volunteer helpers from schools, colleges and universities was to record the then-existing use of every parcel and fragment of land. After editing, the information on the 15,000 field sheets was transferred to outline maps on the scale of 1: 63,360 (1 inch to one mile) for publication. In due course the fully coloured sheets were issued covering the whole of England and Wales, the Isle of Man, and all the more populous parts of Scotland, whilst later an independent survey was carried out for Northern Ireland.

Every sheet presented a complex pattern. Our next task was to analyse that pattern county by county and to try to separate the factors which had led to its evolution: natural factors of elevation, relief, drainage, soil and climate; historical factors, such as ownership, traditional use, access; economic factors such as fluctuating farm prices. Viewed historically, changes in land use, especially over the preceding century, revealed certain trends. The survey and the analysis formed the obvious basis for planning: so often planning is either the encouragement of a trend considered to be good or the reversal of a trend believed to be bad, whilst the initiation of something entirely new, such as a new town or a tract of afforestation, must depend to a considerable extent

STATUS QUO—LAND AND PEOPLE

on the suitability of the natural conditions. So the sequence becomes:

Survey—→analysis—→planning

The first stage is mainly if not completely factual and objective; the second stage involves a considerable degree of subjective judgement. The third stage must be closely related to policy decisions.

The World Land Use Survey

In those countries of the Old World, exemplified by Britain, where human settlement dates back many centuries, indeed millennia, the present land use pattern is fraught with meaning in every detail. In the newer countries, or the sparsely peopled parts of the tropical world, much of the surface cover is natural or semi-natural vegetation; scattered settlements may represent only the first groping efforts of pioneers doomed to failure. In some senses the present pattern of use or non-use of land has far less meaning than in old lands. It is not unnatural, therefore, to find the view, associated with many American workers, that one may safely skip the survey and recording of the present position and proceed straight to preparations for the future by determining 'land capability classes'. If the determination is based on adequate relief, drainage, climate and soil and vegetation surveys, this approach is both scientifically and practically satisfactory, but there is often the unfortunate tendency to plead shortness of time and to map vast areas into land capability class on a subjective snap judgement insufficiently based on fact. In addition work carried out in one country has borne little relationship to that in a neighbouring territory, so that results have not been directly comparable. This is particularly the case with former colonial territories in Africa.

At the Lisbon Conference of the International Geographical Union held in the spring of 1949, Professor Samuel Van Valkenburg, Director of the Graduate School of Geography at Clark University, Worcester, Mass., brought forward a proposal for a World Land Use Inventory. The Congress, with financial help from UNESCO, set up a Commission of five members—Professor Hans Boesch of Zurich, the late Professor Leo Waibel of Minnesota, fresh from years of work in Brazil, Professor Pierre Gourou of Paris and Brussels, and myself, under the chairmanship of Professor Van Valkenburg. Four of us met the following December at Clark, and after a week of meetings and the cross-examination of many experts, and the study of many documents, we drew up a unanimous report with official texts in English, French and German.

In the Report it was pointed out that many, indeed most, countries collected statistics of land use and agriculture, sometimes in very considerable detail, but that it is only in recording the facts on maps that actual distribution can be shown. The Commission then drew up a 'master key' of major categories of land according to existing use or non-use, so that by adopting this common plan, results obtained in one country could be directly compared with those in another. It was not the intention of the Commission, nor is it of the World Land Use Survey which was subsequently set up as a skeleton organization, for a single body to attempt to map the world. With the parallel of the International One-million map of the World, for which the International Geographical Union was the original sponsor fifty years before, the basic idea is to persuade or encourage every country in the world to participate by carrying out its own land use survey, using the common master key, but making as many sub-divisions as may locally be needed.

Early experiments with the use of air-photographs in parts of Africa showed how complex is the pattern even in sparsely inhabited areas which seem monotonous from the ground. It is often a difficult task to show even important detail on anything smaller than a 1: 50,000 scale (or 1 inch to one mile where used) and the 1: 1,000,000 scale originally envisaged for publication must inevitably involve much generalization.

The Commission reported to the Washington Congress of the International Geographical Union in 1952 and to the Rio Congress in 1956. At the latter meeting representatives of the U.S.S.R. and Poland were added and I accepted the Chairmanship as well as undertaking the honorary Directorship of the Survey. Suffice it to say that surveys broadly or exactly along the lines proposed are now in progress in many and diverse lands and map sheets published run into many hundreds. In some countries the work is being handled by an appropriate Government Department set up for the purpose—as in Japan, in Canada for the vast forested north, or the Soil and Land Use Survey of Ghana; the Directorate of Overseas Surveys has undertaken the task for such territories as the Gambia; many governments have commissioned commercial air-survey companies to carry out the work—as in Pakistan, Iraq, Jordan and parts of Sudan; the great international institute at Delft trains workers from all over the world in air-photographic interpretation. The World Land Use Survey has itself undertaken the publication of certain pioneer studies, and memoirs—notably

STATUS QUO—LAND AND PEOPLE

the land use map of Hong Kong and explanatory memoir, and those of Cyprus.

In some countries the classification or basis of work is somewhat different—notably with the fine series of maps prepared under the direction of Professor Henri Gaussen of the University of Toulouse, where the basis is the mapping of vegetation and land use, but the colouring used is related to the interpretation of the facts, rather than the facts themselves. Elsewhere emphasis is placed on soil and direct mapping of land capability classes.

The following, in outline, is the scheme of classification of the World Land Use Survey:

1. *Settlements and associated non-agricultural lands* (red). On the million scale it is recognized that it will only be possible to indicate the larger cities and towns.

2. *Horticulture* (purple). This category is intended to include all intensive cultivation of vegetables and small fruits, as distinct from tree fruits—such as truck farming in America and market gardening in England and other European countries, as well as the production from larger gardens and allotments whether the crops are grown for sale or not, including, for instance, the garden cultivation of tropical villages, as in Malaya.

3. *Tree and other perennial crops* (light purple). The wide range included in this category covers numerous tropical plantations and the orchards of mid-latitudes.

4. *Cropland* (brown) is divided into (a) continual and rotation cropping and (b) land rotation.[1] Continual crops are indicated as meaning, for example, rice, which is often the only crop grown year after year on the same land, and also sugar cane and such monocultural crops as wheat and corn. By rotation crops is understood those grown in a fixed or variable rotation, including fodder grass, clover and alfalfa, which may occupy land for two or three years. Land rotation is the category covering the system whereby cultivation is carried on for a few years and the land then allowed to rest for a considerable period before the scrub or coarse grass is again cleared and the land recultivated. Since this category will cover a very large proportion of the territory in the under-developed countries, its mapping is clearly of the utmost importance. The careless observer is too often misled by what appears to be scrub or second-growth forest and fails to appreciate that it is land being rested in a regular system of land rotation.

[1] Where appropriate, irrigated land is distinguished.

5. *Improved permanent pasture* (managed or enclosed) (light green). This is a type of land use well understood in countries like New Zealand and Britain, where controlled grazing is carried on in small enclosed fields, the grass being managed by manuring, by liming, sometimes by re-seeding, or in other ways. Often the grasses, including clovers, have been introduced so that the pasture is not 'natural'. Some land of this sort is grazed; some is cut for hay or dried grass. In other countries, such as the United States, this category of land is less distinctive, but it would include the intensively stocked grasslands of the American dairy belts.

6. *Unimproved grazing land* (yellow). This may be described as extensive pasture or range land. It may be enclosed in large units but is not, as a rule, in small fields. It is not fertilized or deliberately manured, though it may be periodically burned over. The vegetation is that native to the locality, although its characteristics often have been modified by grazing or occasionally by the introduction of non-local plants. A great range of vegetation is included, from tropical savanna to arctic tundra, and as far as possible the type of vegetation should be described on the map or accompanying notes. For example, this category will include savanna, tropical grassland (e.g. llanos), steppe land, dry pampas and short-grass prairie. The category will also include such range lands as bunch grass and sage brush and creosote bush, as well as the vegetation of the High Veld and the Karroo of South Africa. It will include the heather moorlands and heathlands and grass moorlands of Europe. It is clear that care must be taken to distinguish these very varied types.

There are many areas of such land which at present are not used in different parts of the world, though they differ but little from those which are used for grazing. The Commission's original recommendation to separate used and not used has proved impracticable.

7. *Woodlands* (different shades of green from (5)). Forest and woodland differ greatly from one part of the world to another. The main categories suggested refer to the morphological character of the forest, independently of the age of the trees:

(a) Dense, where the crowns of the trees are touching;
(b) Open, where the crowns of the trees do not touch and the land between is occupied by grass or other ground vegetation. Where trees are sparse such land comes into Category 6 (grazing land);
(c) Scrub, designating vegetation such as the maquis of Europe, chaparral of North America, mallee and mulga of Australia, and the acacia-thorn scrub of Africa and India;
(d) Swamp forests, both fresh-water and tidal;

STATUS QUO—LAND AND PEOPLE

(e) Cut-over or burnt-over forest areas not yet fully reclothed;

(f) Forest with subsidiary cultivation, comprising: (1) shifting cultivation where patches of land are cleared for cultivation from time to time, usually but not always, by wandering tribes; (2) forest-crop economy. Such is the system, for example, in parts of eastern Canada, where holdings consist mainly of woodland, but where some cultivation is carried on subsidiary to the working and management by replanting of the forest land.

8. *Swamps and marshes (fresh- and salt-water, non-forested)* (blue).

9. *Unproductive land* (grey). A great variety of land is also included in this category. Much appears bare, and though it may support lowly forms of plant life, it is essentially unproductive. Barren mountains, rocky and sandy deserts, moving sand-dunes, salt flats, and ice-fields are examples.

A World Population Survey

Parallel with the need for mapping the use or non-use of land is that for the mapping of the present distribution of population. The International Geographical Union at its Rio Congress, during my Presidency, accordingly set up a Commission for the study of this problem under the chairmanship of Professor William William-Olsson of Stockholm. As with land use and agriculture, all countries now collect demographic statistics as discussed above in Chapter II, but comparatively few have officially paid much attention to the areal distribution as shown on maps. In consequence many urgent problems remain to be studied. So often irregularities in population density and distribution, so readily apparent when mapped, are at present very difficult to explain. Areas apparently favoured by physical factors remain—especially in the tropics—almost uninhabited. They naturally invite intensive study in connection with settlement and development projects.

At present there is another very serious gap in factual knowledge as it affects land and people. That is the geographical distribution of pests and diseases and the incidence of the related factors. This applies to pests and diseases which attack man himself (the field of so-called medical geography) as well as his crops and domestic animals.

The population distribution pattern is far from static. Two aspects of change may be specially noted: the decreasing agricultural or rural population and the increasing urban.

STATUS QUO—LAND AND PEOPLE

TABLE XXIV
PERCENTAGE OF EMPLOYED POPULATION ENGAGED IN AGRICULTURE
Data from FAO

	Year	%	Year	%		Year	%	Year	%
Europe					*North America*				
Austria	1934	27	1951	22	Jamaica	1943	44	1950	46
Belgium	1930	20	1950	13	Canada	1931	32	1956	16
Bulgaria	1934	73	—	—	Cuba	1943	41	—	—
Cyprus	1931	51	1950	53	Dominica	1935	77	—	—
Czechoslovakia	1930	33	1950	25	El Salvador	1930	75	—	—
Denmark	1930	34	1950	24	Guatemala	1940	71	1950	61
Finland	1930	64	1950	34	Mexico	1930	67	—	—
France	1931	29	1946	25	Nicaragua	1940	73	—	—
Germany					Panama	1940	52	—	—
(Western)	1939	18	1946	15	Puerto Rico	1940	45	—	—
Greece	1940	53	1949	52	United States	1940	22	1955	13
Hungary	1930	52	1941	49					
Ireland	1936	31	1950	20					
Italy	1931	46	1948	44					
Netherlands	1930	20	1950	14					
Norway	1930	25	1950	19					
Poland	1931	60	1950	46					
Portugal	1940	40	1952	42					
Roumania	1930	72	—	—	*South America*				
Spain	1930	51	1950	48	Brazil	1940	67	—	—
Sweden	1930	31	1950	24	Chile	1930	41	1940	38
Switzerland	1930	22	1950	16	Colombia	1938	74	1951	53
United					Peru	1940	62	—	—
Kingdom	1931	6	1951	5	Venezuela	1941	50	1950	40
Yugoslavia	1931	76	1951	73					
Asia					*Africa*				
Burma	1931	68	—	—	Egypt	1937	70	—	—
India	1931	66	1951	70	Morocco	1936	74	—	—
Indonesia	1930	66	—	—	Nigeria	1931	74	—	—
Japan	1940	43	1952	44	South Africa	1936	64	—	—
Malaya	1931	59	—	—					
Philippines	1939	65	1948	69					
Siam	1937	88	1950	66	*Oceania*				
Turkey	1935	82	1945	72	Australia	1933	23	—	—
China	1937	76	1950	69	New Zealand	1930	24	1950	19

Estimated World Totals
1937: 62 per cent.   1950: 59 per cent.

STATUS QUO—LAND AND PEOPLE

The Agricultural Population

It has often been pointed out in the past that two-thirds of the world's working population is engaged in food production, or in other words that two-thirds of the world's peoples live directly on or from the land, but that for the most part the food produced is inadequate even for the needs of the producer.

In recent years FAO has endeavoured to collect some more detailed statistics in this field and in the *Yearbook* of 1957 reaches the conclusion that agriculture in 1950 occupied 59 per cent of the total population, a drop of 3 per cent since 1937. For many countries the figures are largely guess-work—even those given in Table XXIV must be accepted with much caution. Crude however as they may be, they point inevitably to two conclusions. One is that the proportion of population engaged in farming is decreasing in practically every country in the world. Secondly, it is in general true that a low percentage in agriculture is indicative of a high degree of national development and a high standard of living. Though it cannot be deduced from figures of population, the move is away from complete subsistence farming at the lower levels to a completely commercial agriculture at the higher. It must be noted however that some countries, for example France and Denmark, which enjoy a high standard of living both material and cultural, depend largely on a well-organized and well-balanced agriculture for much of their prosperity.

It is quite wrong to infer—as it is frequently done—that increasing industrialization and a decreasing agriculture are necessarily the panacea for all ills associated with under-development.

Urbanization

The steadily decreasing proportion of the population engaged directly in agriculture is a world-wide phenomenon. Even more marked and universal is the parallel phenomenon of urbanization. Those who cease to work the land do not remain on the land, they drift to the towns. 'Drift' is the right word, for it is rarely a deliberate, purposeful move. Those who find themselves redundant on the land may first pay a casual visit to a neighbouring town to test the chance of employment. The chances are greater in the larger urban centres with a variety of occupational opportunities, hence urbanization is more than just the growth of towns—it is the ever-growing emphasis on the large town. Present-day relationships between town and country are different from those which existed before the development of modern transport—especially by road. The old structure of farm-hamlet-village-country town-administrative centre was a hierarchy essentially interdependent: it was essentially a rural-agricultural pattern. Now the urban-industrial pattern develops independently, spreading over, absorbing and obliterating the older pattern.

What happened in Britain over a long period of years two or three centuries ago is being repeated but with a tremendous concentration in time in most of the less developed countries of today. In Britain the first Agricultural Revolution, involving enclosure of land and improved crop yields from an improved rotation, led to a landless unemployed peasantry who drifted to the towns and became the labour force for the nascent Industrial Revolution. The descendants of these people now constitute four-fifths of the total population; it is they who control the destinies of the nation.

In India the slow improvement of agriculture is a source of anxiety to the planners. Yet improvement to date is estimated to have created in the decade 1947–57 at least 50,000,000 landless peasants, no longer wanted on the land, who have drifted to the towns. There they provide a vast labour reserve for growing industries, but at the same time a source of embarrassment until they can be so absorbed. India at the census of 1931 had 103 towns of over 50,000, of which 38 were over 100,000 but only 2 had reached a million. In 1951 India and Pakistan together had at least 200 towns over 50,000, of which 88 were over 100,000 and 6 over a million.

A phenomenon of special interest is the growth of the so-called 'millionaire city'—of over a million inhabitants. In a recent paper,[1] Professor David Linton has given reasons for believing that the world had 24 such cities in the early nineteen-twenties, 39 in the nineteen-thirties, 41 in the early nineteen-forties and 80 in the early or mid-nineteen-fifties. He estimates that during that period the total population in such cities had increased from 51 millions to 192·5 and from 2·86 per cent of total world population to 7·66. In his words, 'despite the quite fantastic rate at which world total population is growing, the number of its peoples who live in millionaire cities is growing even more

[1] D. L. Linton, 'Millionaire Cities Today and Yesterday', *Geography*, 43, 1958, 253–8.

STATUS QUO—LAND AND PEOPLE

rapidly, so that they form a rapidly increasing percentage of the whole.'

What is actually happening rather makes nonsense of attempts by some planners to limit the growth of cities; it suggests that our efforts should be directed towards perfecting the urban environment rather than towards attempts, which must inevitably prove abortive, at dispersal. As food production becomes more efficient and concentrated in the hands of the experts who produce professionally for the masses, so the subsistence farmer and peasant producer would seem to be doomed. What is perhaps the still greater problem then arises: what shall be the occupations of the countless millions displaced from the land?

XI
POOR LITTLE RICH GIRL

The picture, one might almost say fable, of the poor little rich girl is a familiar one. She is usually represented as motherless and fatherless but with limitless wealth, which enables her to be surrounded by all the material goods that money can buy. But by these very circumstances she is isolated and lonely. Are those who seek to guide, direct and help her really her friends, or have even the most seemingly kindly some ulterior motive? Can she have friends on her own level? They feel unable to give her anything, for she already has all; if she gives to them, a small gift may seem mean, a big one savours of patronage or charity which engenders hate rather than love. She may be young and inexperienced but she has greatness thrust upon her. She is expected to lend her support to this project and that, to supply funds but then to sit back and not interfere with the running of affairs by her elders and, presumably, betters. How will she shape when she grows to maturity? Isolated still—for that there can be no remedy except perhaps for a few in more or less the same position who may well be deadly rivals rather than friends. Will she be bitter and disillusioned by the ungrateful attitude of the poor relations she has honestly tried to help? Or will she continue her attempts to help those around her despite rebuffs and criticisms so often unmerited? Will she try to retire to enjoy her own house and garden, letting the world go hang?

Among the nations it is obvious how closely the description of the poor little rich girl fits the United States.

By any standard the United States is rich. Taking first the particular aspect emphasized in this book, every American citizen has a share of the homeland amounting to 10·6 acres, or 12·5 if Alaska is included. The bulk lies in mid-latitudes and even if as much as a half suffers from elevation or ruggedness, aridity or absence of soil, there remain 5 acres of potentially useful land as defined in Chapter III. Though there is no official estimate of land available as there is in Canada, we have such

POOR LITTLE RICH GIRL

pronouncements as that of J. D. Black and M. E. Kiefer (*Future Food and Agriculture Policy*, 1948) that 'if the land of the United States were in Europe probably some 700,000,000 acres would be cropped in some sort of rotation'. In fact the total of 'improved land' in farms is of the order of 530,000,000 acres or about 3 acres per head. Vast areas in the eastern States which the Pilgrim Fathers and their early successors cleared of forest and laboriously fenced or walled into fields now lie abandoned as agriculturally submarginal. Overall shortage of land is not a problem though local adjustments of people and land may be. In truth America's far-flung farmlands have become an *embarras de richesse*. Casually cultivated in an extensive system abundant food for the nation, and some for export, together with huge quantities of raw materials such as cotton, were easily produced. With the application of even some of the methods of the new Agricultural Revolution acre-yields have shot up to such an extent that over-production and surpluses have become a vital problem. As I attempted to demonstrate in my original Patten Lectures, if one considers 'under-development' to mean under-development of land and other potential resources, the United States was amongst the greatest of the under-developed giants of the world.

If America has claims to riches as a primary producer on her farms and pastures, so she has in her mines and quarries. With the largest reserves and production of coal in the world; the largest production of oil in the world, the largest production of natural gas in the world, the greatest potential and development of water power, the world's largest uranium mine and important reserves of fissionable material, the power position is very strong.

In minerals there are huge productions and still vast reserves of iron ore, gold, silver, copper, lead, zinc and many other metals—only tin as almost the solitary exception. America has had the raw materials, the capital and the skill to build up vast manufacturing industries whose production is geared to supply more than the home market. So this great nation is able to provide the world with a large range of foodstuffs, some raw materials and an almost limitless range of manufactured goods. But what is wanted in exchange? A few items of tropical and equatorial origin which cannot be home produced—notably rubber, coffee, cocoa and tea; some commodities so extravagantly used that home supplies do not keep pace with demand—notably timber and wood pulp; a few items of luxury character for which home conditions are unsuitable, notably silk. The position would be difficult enough if

POOR LITTLE RICH GIRL

an entirely unrestricted inflow of commodities and goods in exchange were allowed; instead most industrialists live back in the days where their nascent efforts needed protection and this they continue to demand and even to extend. Further the financial control of so much of the world's trade enables the United States in many cases to name both terms and prices so that primary producers in the undeveloped countries find themselves at the mercy of the big bosses.

America as a nation, like Americans as individuals, is almost incred-

TABLE XXV
GIANTS COMPARED

Percentage of World Total

	United States	U.S.S.R.	British Commonwealth
Land	6	15	20
People	6	7	—
Wealth	40	?	—
Minerals:			
Bauxite	7	6	39
Aluminium production	45	16	17
Asbestos	3	—	90
Chrome ore	4	15	34
Coal	21	20	16
Cobalt	13	—	25
Copper	27	13	26
Diamonds	—	—	70
Gold	4	40	50
Iron ore	25	19	13
Pig iron output	35	17	11
Steel output	35	17	12
Lead ore	13	14	26
Manganese	3	40	26
Nickel ore	4	16	55
Petroleum	40	11	12
Phosphate rock	44	18	7
Silver	18	ex	25
Tin ore	—	?	43
Tungsten	12	ex	8
Uranium ore	28	ex	44
Zinc	16	10	25
Wheat	13	20[1]	18
Corn (Maize)	50	4[1]	5
Cotton	31	15	14

[1] Very rough estimates based on acreage.
ex = excluded from statistics available.

POOR LITTLE RICH GIRL

ibly generous in pouring out vast sums of money to help the underdeveloped countries. It is the American taxpayers' money freely and ungrudgingly given. The money enables the recipients to purchase the foodstuffs and raw materials and, more especially, the machinery and manufactures they so badly need and which are to a large extent available from America. Why does not this open-handed generosity meet, in the long run, with the appreciation it surely deserves? Simply because it is charity. It engenders jealousy and hate. There is not a country in the world which would not rather receive a good price and an open market for its produce in the United States. A succinct letter in *The Times* of 17th January 1959 puts it so well for the two-thirds of mankind living in Asia:

'From an Asian point of view the battle for Asia is not an ideological battle. It is a battle for bread, rice and shelter. Asia has nothing to offer but her jute, oil and tin to sell. Infinitely more valuable than any assistance would be a decent price for its commodities. It is time someone as great as Keynes proclaimed that pricing by the 'interplay of free trade' is nothing but organized loot when the trade is between economic unequals, and that as within any single nation, so between nations, isolated prosperity cannot survive long. The battle for Asia will be won by whichever world bloc realizes this truth first.'

A. RASHID.

So the poor little rich girl, by her very magnanimity in one direction, is driving her friends to seek the wicked uncle. There are often aspects of her behaviour which make the position worse. She is afraid of being dependent on others and so seeks to make her position impregnable in various ways. I shall not attempt in my own words to explain the dilemma of the United States: I shall leave that to an American, C. Lester Walker. He has ably summarized the position for the general reader in an article in the *American Mercury* (December 1949) under the title: 'No Wonder the World is Short of Dollars.' In large measure the result of a position forced on her by two world wars, in part the result of a restless urge to find a substitute for anything which cannot be home-produced, the United States has reached the fantastic level of self-sufficiency wherein she produces 94 per cent or more of all goods consumed within the country, and with one-sixteenth of the world's population is producing nearly one-third of the world's goods. Synthetic rubber has replaced the import of natural rubber from south-east Asia, synthetic mica the natural product from India (the production of syn-

POOR LITTLE RICH GIRL

thetic mica is, in fact, still in the laboratory stage), synthetic nitrate the natural product from Chile, nylon the silk from Japan and China, tough paper the jute from India, synthetic cryolite the natural mineral from Greenland. The home-produced article has now replaced more or less completely the once-large imports of dyestuffs, optical glass and toys (from Germany), watches (Switzerland), chewing gum (Mexico), cigarette paper (France), bristles (China), insecticides (East Africa) and many others. Home agricultural developments have affected almost every part of the world—as with soya beans (formerly entirely from Manchuria), figs (Turkey), currants, sultanas and raisins (Greece, Turkey), wines (Spain and France), sugar (West Indies), dates (Iraq and North Africa), and rice (south-east Asia).

Forward-thinking Americans are alive to the situation: there is no need for me as an Englishman to attempt to assess the position other than by quoting American sources. What has been happening over the past few years? First I may repeat what I wrote in *Our Undeveloped World*. Side by side with this development is an embarrassing overproduction of agricultural commodities—a story of plentiful stocks of food which once again seem doomed to deterioration, decay and destruction in the midst of a hungry, sometimes starving, world. This is the way in which the position was presented to millions of readers through the magazine *Fortune* in January 1950, relayed by the *Reader's Digest* in April 1950:

'The U.S. Government's farm price-support programme . . . has erected a falsework of bogus values under the whole farm economy, which would collapse into ruin if the support were suddenly removed. It is forcing farmers to produce wildly in excess of any reasonable American capacity to consume. . . . The Government lost 204 million dollars by destroying potatoes or selling them for less than the price of their bags . . . fed millions of dollars' worth of California raisins to hogs. The United States Commodity Credit Corporation is left with a fantastic two-billion-dollar inventory:

'Nearly 5,000,000 bales of cotton—worth about $750,000,000,
'nearly 400,000,000 bushels of wheat costing around $900,000,000,
'nearly 600,000,000 bushels of corn worth around $900,000,000,
'more than 70,000,000 lb. of dried eggs costing close to $100,000,000,
'more than 100,000,000 lb. of butter costing more than $60,000,000,
'about 250,000,000 lb. of dried milk worth over $30,000,000,
'huge stocks of tobacco . . . dried fruit, turpentine and rosin . . . wool, soybeans, turkeys, (and) peanuts. . . .

POOR LITTLE RICH GIRL

'There is little hope that CCC's colossal inventory will melt away. On the contrary present farm policies are bound to increase it . . . The Department of Agriculture's other solution is to limit output. . . . The Department has asked farmers to cut acreage of wheat, cotton, potatoes, peanuts and tobacco, and whether this will cut production is another thing. Better seed and more fertilizer may well maintain output despite somewhat smaller acreage.'[1]

All this is happening within the Dollar Curtain, and it seems to bear no relationship to the position in the rest of the world. Over the same period there is no doubt whatever that uncounted thousands died of malnutrition or starvation in Africa and Asia. Even the British housewife was unable to buy, at any price, through ordinary trade channels, a single pound of those California raisins.

This was ten years ago. In the meantime Government attempts to restrict agricultural output have been made more difficult by acre-yields boosted by technical progress (see pp. 80–89 above), and the stock piles remain.

The recording of stocks of the major agricultural commodities is now part of the work regularly undertaken by FAO. Let us see how stocks on 1st July 1957 compare with those given above for 1949:

	United States stocks	
	1949	1957
Cotton bales	5,000,000	11,000,000
Wheat bushels	400,000,000	900,000,000
Corn (maize) bushels	600,000,000	1,650,000,000
Butter, lb.	100,000,000	90,000,000
Milk, dried, lb.	250,000,000	100,000,000

The stock pile of wheat reached a high of 28,200,000 metric tons (1,036,000,000 bushels) in 1955, the stock pile of coarse grains (maize, rye, barley, oats and sorghum) has risen with monotonous regularity, and was estimated on 1st July 1957 to have reached the fantastic level of 57,500,000 metric tons, or over 2,000,000,000 bushels. Cotton stocks reached a high of 3,140,000 tons in 1956.

To some extent, Canada with a stock of 19,900,000 tons (730,000,000 bushels) of wheat on 1st August 1957, shares the stock problems of the United States. Indeed, taking the world stocks of key agricultural products, the United States and Canada hold three-quarters of the whole.

---

[1] By special permission of the editors of *Fortune*.

POOR LITTLE RICH GIRL

In an address delivered on 24th October 1958, entitled 'American Business and World Leadership', Mr. Murray D. Lincoln, President of Nationwide Insurance, quoted Calvin Coolidge as responsible, some thirty years ago, for saying that the business of America is business which he would now change by saying the business of America is no longer just business: it is also nothing less than world leadership. 'This big, good-natured country of ours', he continues, 'has been much too busy making money, living luxuriously, playing games, watching games, and just having itself one big ball of fun.'

What does the assumption of world leadership involve? Whatever practical or theoretical answer may be given to this question, what is involved at the present moment is the expansion of the Dollar Empire.

The World's Greatest Empire

That old hackneyed adage 'history repeats itself' rather omits to note that in the repetition there are usually differences. From the days of the first written records of the activities of mankind there have been empires to rise and fall. The fact that the greatest empire of all time—which has arisen almost entirely within the last forty years, since the end of the First World War, is an economic empire and so different from its political predecessors, should not be allowed to obscure the fact that it is an empire and that in its various manifestations it parallels the empires of past times.

At least in their own judgement the world's great empire builders have usually been activated by the highest motives. When the Romans swept across the narrow straits to conquer barbarian Britain it was in the knowledge that they might confer the advantages of a sophisticated urban society on an undeveloped and savage land, that they might do something through their culture and religion expressed in magnificent buildings to lighten the way for the unenlightened, some of whom in due course might qualify for that proud title *civis romanus*—and become a Roman citizen. When the Spanish Conquistadores following in the path blazed by Christopher Columbus swept over the lands which now form Latin America it was with the triple objective of Gospel, Glory and Gold. The makers of the British Empire had no doubts as to their duty in conferring upon the savages and heathens of the world the advantages of law and order long summed up in the words *Pax Britannica* coupled with those material advances consequent upon trade following the flag. As recently as the last two decades of the nineteenth century Cecil John Rhodes in his ambition to 'paint the whole of Africa red' saw the only African road to progress and prosperity as under the British flag with American support. Quite simply and with all modesty he believed the English-speaking peoples had followed the highest ideals of justice, liberty and peace, and that God had called upon Britain and America to rule the world for its own good. He regarded the split between the United States and Britain as the greatest tragedy of history, one day to be remedied. For the gigantic task of bringing the whole world under one beneficent government, he allotted himself Africa. He sought to amass a vast personal fortune in order to carry out his own Point IV programme. His objectives live on in the Rhodes Scholarships.

The architects of the Dollar Empire inherit the high ideals of previous Empire builders, perhaps some of their faults; certainly they are compelled to adopt and adapt most of the devices of their predecessors. Because they work at a time when words like empire, colonization and even culture have become suspect and taboo, we almost fail to recognize the *civis romanus sum* in the U.S. Passport, the silver penny of the New Testament current from the Atlantic to the Indian Ocean in the dollar bill, the gospel of good tidings in the American Way of Life, or that Coca-colonization is just the new economic form of colonization.

The great rivalries of the Middle Ages of Spain and Portugal, of Holland and France and Britain have been replaced today by the clash of ideologies with the vague West and Communism in the chief roles.

Although there is a fervent belief at home, and a tacit acceptance with some reservations elsewhere, that the American Way of Life enshrines the ideals of a modern world, it is not easy to define what is meant. It would almost seem as if each of the many million users of the phrase has a personal interpretation. During my stay at the University of Indiana the essential meaning of the American Way of Life was a constant source of discussion: when the energies of a whole nation are devoted to the spreading of a gospel one really ought to know what the gospel implies. It was at Indiana that a great scholar, the blind Professor Fields, after one such discussion lasting late into the night, typed out for me his own interpretation, five pages of close-spaced typescript, embodying some of the contradictions of the code.

With a concept of the American Way of Life in mind, what can we say of its spread over the world—the American or Dollar Empire? First, it is the product of the last forty years. A reluctant United States was forced to join in the First World War, but even after that the old isolation won, and Woodrow Wilson failed to lead his own country to back his own creation, the League of Nations. But within a few years the flag was compelled to follow trade—the trade interests established by American investors seeking outlets for their funds, by American business interests seeking to safeguard new supplies of oil and the raw materials of which home supplies might be getting scarce.

In due course the home fortress was consolidated and its defences strengthened. Within the 3 million square miles of continental United States there is free trade and an almost complete freedom of movement, but the whole is surrounded by a succession of defences. Consistently with the advantages to be enjoyed when entry is granted, entry into the United States is probably as difficult as into any country in the world. It is automatically excluded, except for V.I.P's in special circumstances, to a third of all mankind, the Communists, even as temporary visitors. Entry for purposes of residence is limited by a rigid quota system for all nations, and applicants must accept the major tenets of the American Way of Life and be of the right skin colour. The entry of goods into the United States is likewise controlled very strictly by a complex and forbidding tariff wall, and much paper in quintuplicate.

From earliest times the defence of a homeland has depended both upon the obvious defensive works on the borders and also upon distant outposts. In times past these were obtained by negotiation, settlement, or conquest. The general pattern has changed little over the centuries and the fortified outpost bases are as important as ever but are now usually acquired by lease. In times past, when the major powers felt unable to trust the laws and justice of the countries in which military or trading bases were situated, they introduced the principle of extraterritoriality, claiming the right to subject their own nationals to their own laws and not to the laws of the country concerned. It was a convenient system, but led to much international friction and it was regarded as a victory for democracy when it was finally abolished in such places as Shanghai, Shameen (Canton) and other cities of China where it had lingered long. America has, however, found it necessary to reintroduce the system for their service personnel overseas and sometimes the principle is carried to extreme lengths—as when United States firms with premises on foreign soil demand all payments in dollars and refuse to recognize the local currency. Once more history repeats itself.

Both in defence and the protection of trade and commerce, overseas bases and trading posts have always relied on the maintenance of good communications. The development of empires by the European Powers.

especially after the Treaty of Berlin in 1880, led to the great development of sea communications by Britain, France, Germany, the Netherlands, Belgium, Italy and other countries each primarily concerned in the first instance to link colonies and homeland. The modern emphasis is on air travel and transport, but the principle is the same. American and American-controlled lines boast the largest world network of airlines and emphasize the world-wide ramifications of the American Economic Empire—excluding only the Soviet bloc.

The world-wide character of American trade is at once apparent in the direction of exports and imports. Few parts of the habitable world are not now regularly visited by American business men and tourists. American advertising is so essentially a part of American business that it has brought the roadside hoarding to the destruction of taste and beauty in half the world. The full extent of American investment in overseas countries is hard to gauge: as with all international investment it is complicated by varied financial holdings in indigenous companies. But the world-wide familiarity with such names as Woolworth, Ford, General Motors, Standard Oil or Esso, and Singer, is evidence enough.

Obviously this investment is far from unremunerative. Whereas Empire builders in the past were content, often compelled, to sink vast sums of the home taxpayers' money with little hope of return, the economic imperialist is free to withdraw when his ventures do not pay. Handsome dividends are drawn from overseas investments. Is this exploitation? Does the sale of a commodity such as C—— C—— confer a benefit on the purchasers commensurate with the 10 or 20 or 50 per cent drawn by home shareholders?

It is a major tragedy that Americans, who stand theoretically for democracy, freedom and equality of opportunity, should automatically introduce a class distinction into any country where they may reside or work. Especially in the under-developed countries is their disruption of the local economy seemingly inevitable. It is no fault of the individual American that his home standard of living is so high as to put him apart from the world as a whole, that American currency is so sought after as to make the dollar very expensive in terms of other currencies. It is natural that an American willing to live and work abroad should receive some compensation over and above what would be his normal salary at home. Translated into terms of any local currency he is automatically in the top flight. In many countries the salary of a young executive is that of the local prime minister, an American stenographer's is that of the Ambassador or Chargé d'Affaires of another country.

POOR LITTLE RICH GIRL

The creation of a *herrenvolk* is obvious. Where accommodation is short the local resident is outbid every time; the very desire to pay what seems only a reasonable wage to staff completely disrupts the local economy. Jealousy and hate are so closely allied: the results are inevitable. Over so much of the world nothing is more precious than 'face'. To save face it is essential to try and match up to the standard of the stranger: a single meal light-heartedly accepted as a token of goodwill may mean a month's salary to the giver.

Let us be quite clear that a large proportion of these residents overseas are actuated by the highest motives. They are engaged in the export of 'know-how', they hope earnestly to improve the hard lot of those among whom they work. It is a sacrifice of home comforts and amenities to live and work amid primitive surroundings. In all these respects they share with the servants of the home government in old colonial days. The District administrator—call him D.C. or whatever was the appropriate title—dedicated his life to the service of the people—in truth so often his children—of his district. Responsible for law and order he made possible the working of the technical expert—the Agricultural Officer, the Forestry Officer, the Educational Officer, each dedicated to conservation of resources and the improvement of the prosperity of the people. The modern technical expert has the same objectives but without the responsibilities.

Reference was made above to the impassioned plea, the heart-cry of almost every under-developed country, for good prices and a stable market for their primary products. Let us take just two examples of products coming almost exclusively from the less developed tropical countries—cocoa and rubber. Cocoa is a particularly good example; because it is not a plantation crop higher prices do not go into the pockets of distant shareholders, but to the multitude of small growers. The average price of the 2,000,000,000 lb. which entered world markets in 1956 was about 26 U.S. cents per lb. Had the price ruling in 1954 of 57 U.S. cents per lb. been maintained, an additional $620,000,000 or £220,000,000 would have flowed into the coffers of Ghana, Nigeria, the Cameroons, French West Africa and Brazil—money proudly earned, not received in charity. Similarly with rubber, had the price of 1951 (56 U.S. cents per lb.) been maintained (in 1954 23 U.S. cents); much of the extra $1,320,000,000 (£470,000,000) would have remained to benefit Malaya, Indonesia, Ceylon, North Borneo, Thailand and India.

POOR LITTLE RICH GIRL

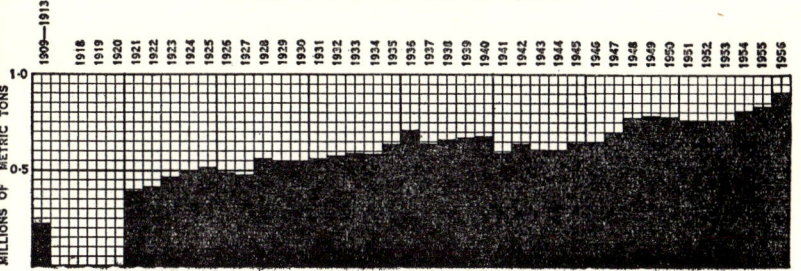

Fig. 39
Graph of World Production of Cocoa

This graph shows a steady almost uninterrupted rise in the world production and demand for cocoa—used especially in the form of chocolate consumed especially in the developed countries. Clearly cocoa ought to provide the less-developed countries, where it is produced, with a steadily rising income. Unfortunately, this is far from being the case because of widely fluctuating prices

XII

POOR RELATIONS
THE UNDER-DEVELOPED COUNTRIES

It is curious how quickly certain words—presumably the same is true in any language—come to take on a special meaning which is resented by the people to whom they are applied. People in Britain will recall how the depression of the 'thirties hit certain industrial areas with such severity that special legislative measures were taken to alleviate the sufferings of these 'Depressed Areas'. But within a matter of months the people were objecting to the designation Depressed Areas and so they became the Special Areas. Then exception was taken to the term 'Special' and so they became 'Development Areas'. Somewhat similarly when the spirit of the United Nations Charter swept the world after the Second World War leading countries began to realize their responsibilities for the 'backward areas'—except that no country liked to be referred to as backward. Peoples living in the 'backward areas' felt that the term conveyed both an unjust judgement and a reproach. If their countries were indeed backward, might it not be that they laboured under handicaps not imposed on the more fortunate, might it not be that they were victims of historical and economic circumstances beyond their control or even of past and present suppression or repression? Still more important, might it not also be that areas classed as backward in material progress were actually the homes of ethical, moral and religious codes which had much to teach the Western World? So in the place of 'backward' the words under-developed or undeveloped came into general use, especially after the famous Point IV of President Truman in his Inaugural Address on 20th January 1949.

'Fourth, we must embark on a bold new programme for making the benefits of our scientific advances and industrial progress available for the improvement and growth of under-developed areas. More than half the people of the world are living in conditions approaching misery. Their food is inadequate. They are victims of disease. Their economic

POOR RELATIONS

life is primitive and stagnant. Their poverty is a handicap and a threat to them and to more prosperous areas. For the first time in history, humanity possesses the knowledge and the skill to relieve the suffering of these people.'

Truman, it should be noted, referred first to miserable conditions, then to inadequate food, disease and a stagnant economy. The assessment is essentially on economic grounds. But what really constitutes 'under-development'? There exists what may be called an 'official' definition—that used to determine whether a country is eligible for United States' assistance under the Point IV programme. This was based on income *per capita*. If the income per head of population falls below a certain figure, the country is classed as under-developed. Although the result may be satisfactory from the point of view of the aid programme, it would seem that it is poverty, not under-development, which is being measured. To take a hypothetical case, there might not be a single farmer in the United States but, provided the income of the people remained above the datum line, the country could not be classed as 'under-developed'. On the other hand, by this definition India and China, even in their most crowded and intensively cultivated parts, are under-developed.

The Statistical Office of the United Nations in the study published in 1951 on the National Income in Under-Developed Countries, however, does not attempt to define under-developed but uses it as contrasted to industrialized.

Taking the words literally, there is the obvious interpretation of under-developed—the natural resources have not been developed to the full extent possible. The greatest of all natural resources is land, and there are parts of the world, in the Yangtse Delta, for example, where the produce of a single square mile is sufficient to support several thousand human beings. There are some parts of India where a rural density of 1,000 a square mile prevails. Can we possibly class such lands as under-developed though the people may live in conditions approaching misery, handicapped in every direction by poverty?

Well-farmed European lands support one person or more an acre, 640 or more to the square mile, yet lands we think of as 'developed' by our modern Western methods, in the United States, Canada and Argentina, produce only enough food on a square mile to support some 200 or 240 persons. On the basis of output per acre we find the familiar mid-latitude or temperate lands of North America amongst the most under-developed lands in the world. If the object of 'development' is to achieve maximum production or to support a maximum population, we have a long way to go before we can regard our own lands as fully developed. Yet the techniques of which we boast have been worked out to meet conditions as we know them best.

It is to be noted that recently the words 'undeveloped' and 'underdeveloped' themselves are coming to be regarded with disfavour. We find now FAO in *The State of Food and Agriculture* 1958 officially dividing the world into 'Developed Regions'—Western Europe, North America and Oceania—and into 'Less Developed Regions'—Latin America, Far East, Near East and Africa. These regions are shown in Fig. 40.

If, however, we turn to the older basis of assessing degrees of development by national income *per capita*, we get the interesting position that there are some countries, especially those which have benefited by recent development of oil resources, which stand out from their neighbours in quite startling fashion. This is clearly shown in Fig. 41.

The Less Developed Countries in World Economy

It is interesting to note the close parallel which often exists between human relationships which exist within a family and the international relationships which are found within the human family. The wealthy or prosperous individual often finds it difficult, even impossible, to realize that a poor relation may prefer his own way of life, that he may even find greater happiness in a simple life with few needs, few responsibilities, but above all independence. The more developed nations find it hard to understand the ideas and ideals of many of the less developed countries. There is no doubt of the reality of the upsurge of nationalism: the preference for independence even with bad government than for good rule and material progress under alien rule. In this sense political colonialism belongs to the past. But to exchange political colonialism for economic colonialism is out of the frying-pan into the fire: almost without exception the developing countries desire economic independence as fiercely as they desire political independence, but the issue is not so clear.

What have they to offer as the price of their economic independence? Primarily their raw materials: animal, vegetable and mineral, above all mineral. Colonial powers in the past have been accused, often with very little justification, of exploitation. As we have already observed,

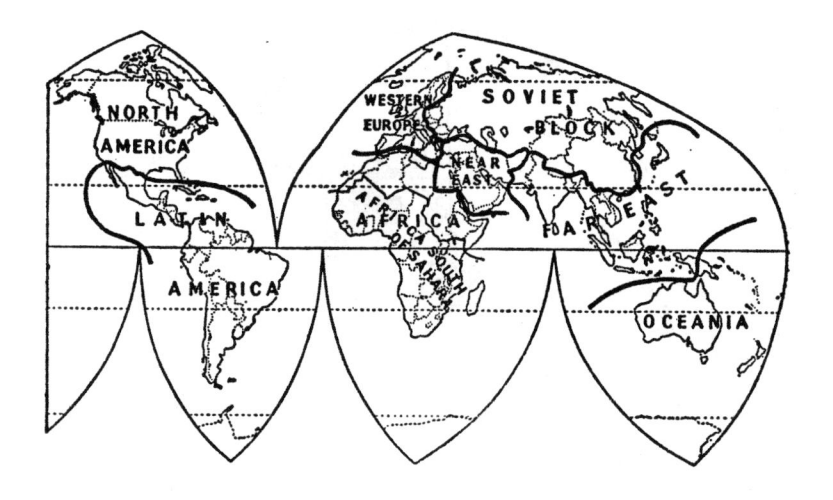

Fig. 40

The Division of the World into Developed Regions and Less Developed Regions as used by FAO, 1958

economic exploitation is a very real danger today, but often just as difficult to assess in rights and wrongs as ever in the past. Take the familiar example of oil. Before there can be any financial return vast sums must be spent in exploration, then in development. In many cases expenditure in exploration will produce no results, and must be written off. If success comes, the financial reward is, and should be, great. Yet at that stage the cry of exploitation may be raised, 50–50 shares in profits regarded as inadequate, and a handful of nationalist firebrands may demand—and carry out—expropriation. Yet, as Table XXVI shows, the less developed countries already make a major contribution to world economy in their contribution of much-needed minerals.

Speaking generally, industrial leaders in the developed countries can have little direct interest in the development of those commodities, notably food, which the less developed countries need for themselves. Yet indirectly their interest is very great and with very few exceptions the great international industrial and commercial concerns are foremost in fostering education, health and technical services and indeed all aspects of progress in countries from which they are deriving their raw materials. There is today full realization that a slum nation is as much a menace to the world as a slum is to a developing city.

That there are contrary influences we have already noted—unstable

Fig. 41

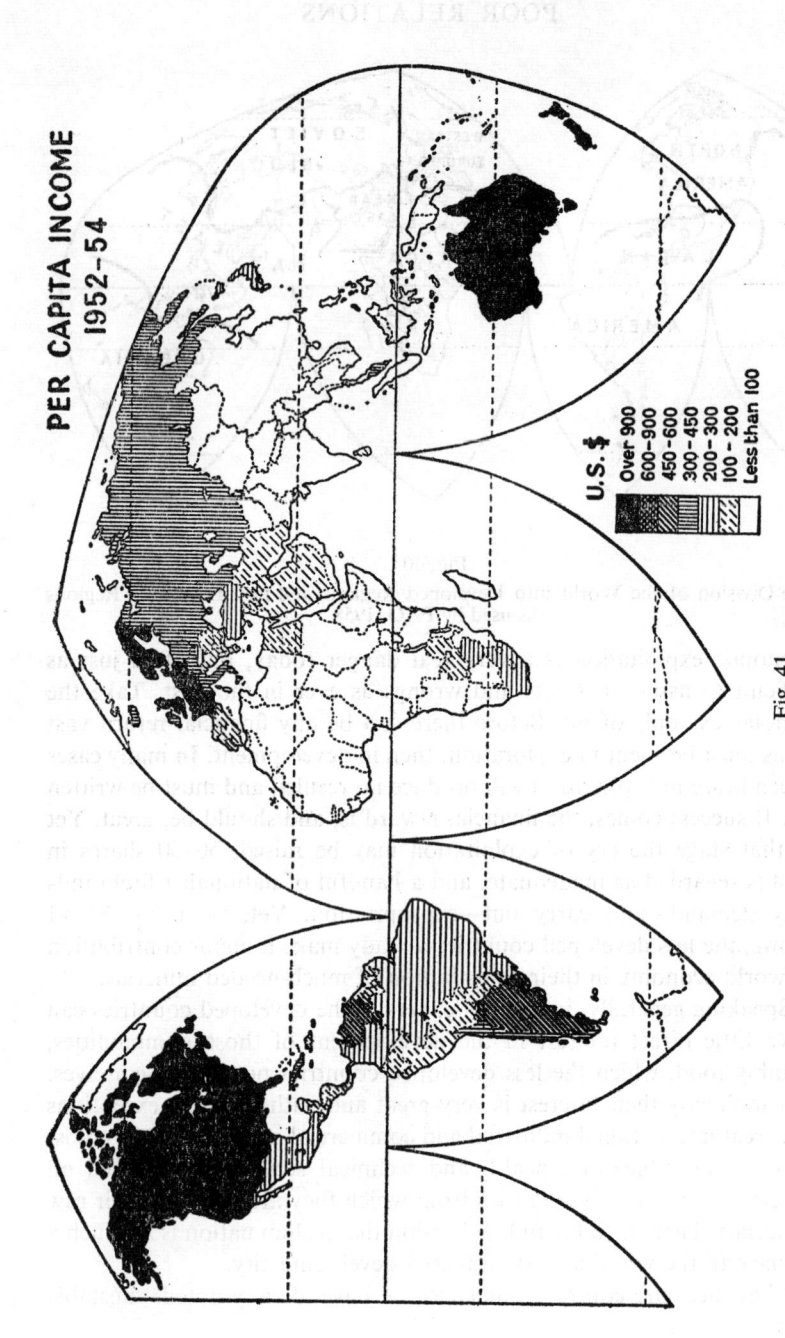

National Incomes *Per Capita* (in part after D. W. Fryer, *Econ. Geog.*, 1958)

prices, tariff barriers and other import–export restrictions—and again it must be underlined that aid can never replace self-help.

TABLE XXVI

CONTRIBUTIONS TO WORLD ECONOMY FROM LESS DEVELOPED COUNTRIES

Minerals	Percentage of World Production
Bauxite	61
Aluminium	1
Asbestos	12
Chrome ore	40
Coal	5
Cobalt ore	75
Copper	40
Diamonds	100
Gold	6
Iron ore	12
Pig iron	4
Steel	4
Lead	30
Manganese	42
Nickel ore	36
Petroleum	44
Phosphate rock	32
Silver ore	48
Tin ore	95
Zinc ore	28

Less developed countries are those shown as such in Fig. 40.

The figures for aluminium compared with bauxite; iron and steel compared with iron ore show that the less developed countries provide much of the raw material, but the material is processed elsewhere.

XIII

QUO VADIS?

My main purpose in writing this book has been to set out in plain language some of the great world problems of the day as I see them stemming from the overriding dilemma of people outgrowing space. It is not my purpose, even if I were able, to answer the questions posed and certainly not to suggest remedies, cures and solutions. But it is surely the duty of every thinking and voting citizen to try and appreciate the significance of world trends. We are called upon to take action to remedy the ills of the moment but without due thought may be making the solution of long-term problems more difficult.

So many and diverse factors enter into the problems of our developing world that I have felt compelled to touch perfunctorily on a great variety of topics. I am conscious that the result is a ragged whole far from satisfactory, and in this final chapter I can do no more than emphasize a few of the lessons to be drawn rather than state conclusions.

World Population

There can be no doubt of the present rapid increase in world population. It is clear that this cannot continue indefinitely. That 'standing room' only is within a measurable span of years, about 600, short even in terms of past history, makes it clear that a major change cannot be far ahead. The fundamental thesis of Malthus was that population, unchecked, increases in a geometrical ratio, the means of subsistence only in arithmetical ratio, and that population always increases up to the limits of the means of subsistence and is only checked by war, famine, pestilence, and the influence of miseries derived from a consequent low standard of living. The third check of Malthus—pestilence—has so far been conquered that the main causes of death, despite the

QUO VADIS?

names given to them in medical statistics, are those natural to old age, when the human machine, having clocked up 70, 80 or 90 years, wears out. Even so medical skill continues to prolong life and we can look forward to a steadily increasing proportion of old people. With regard to the fourth check of Malthus, an all-out and world-wide drive to improve living standards is in full swing: the physical 'misery' of which Malthus wrote is likely to give place to the mental misery of a world rent by cold wars. The second check of Malthus—famine—is much more real. Instantaneous and world-wide communication by radio and ever-increasing facilities of physical communication have removed the dangers of local famine in the old sense. Clearly world-wide shortage of food is not just round the corner: with existing agricultural techniques widely applied, the world could probably support four or five times its present population: but those techniques are at present being vastly and rapidly improved under the new agricultural revolution, whilst the cultivation of the sea has not yet begun. Wide-scale famine, the starvation of nations, could only result from the operation of those man-made barriers which we have come to call 'curtains'—the Iron Curtain, the Dollar Curtain, the Bamboo Curtain and others not yet named. With a continued existence of man-made barriers, starvation of nations could easily happen, even at the present time, and we are brought up against the dilemma facing every crowded country—but particularly Britain and certain of her continental neighbours. The one argument is that Britain as a manufacturing country can best continue in that role, importing food from countries compelled or preferring to specialize in primary production. Accepting that view, we have no special need to protect our own farm land from housing and industrial development. If our people wish a spacious garden and large tracts, essentially unproductive and devoted to recreation, we need not worry. Those who hold this currently fashionable view need to be reminded how nearly Britain was reduced to starvation in two world wars, and that national existence precariously balanced on the knife-edge of maintained export trade presents a terrifying prospect. Those who take the more cautious long-term view argue that, whatever the economic position of the moment, we should not destroy the means of subsistence for the future. What is the sense in covering productive agricultural land with bricks and mortar when other equally suitable sites can be found, what is the sense of building new towns for future generations to starve in when gracious urban living can be achieved, they argue, by redeveloping, perhaps living high in flats, existing towns.

QUO VADIS?

What can we say of the check to human population which Malthus put first—war? Only that mankind now has the means to wipe itself out, and that it only needs a handful of madmen out of the world's 3,100,000,000 inhabitants to do so.

The Estate of Man

The late Michael Roberts at the time of his much lamented death in 1948 had almost completed the typescript of a book of wide scope which was subsequently published, posthumously, under the title, *The Estate of Man*.[1] In one particularly striking chapter he contrasts what man has done to improve his domestic animals and his cultivated plants by selective breeding with what man is deliberately doing with his own race. Through the increasing spread of medical skill we keep alive the diseased, the deformed, mental and physical degenerates. We do not in any way discourage them from breeding. Indeed the whole trend of legislation is the other way. Class and privilege have become dirty words in our declared intention of raising the standards of the masses, we tax during life and after death the intelligentsia and the successful pioneer to such an extent that they are barely able to propagate their kind. Michael Roberts saw in this a dangerous lowering of the sum total of human intellectual and physical standards, in that a general rise in the standard of intelligence and stamina of the masses did not balance the loss of what might have been achieved through a select few. Our world today is a world of conflicting ideologies: it may well be that the first group to solve this dilemma will be the one to survive.

Town and Country

It is abundantly clear that man is fast becoming an urban animal. Rural depopulation either actual or relative to total population is coupled with the growth of towns, especially of the large cities, and notably those with over a million inhabitants. The production from land and sea of food and raw materials is rapidly becoming the occupation of the specialist farmer, forester and fisherman, using all the refinements of method modern science and human organization can devise. Even at the present time the whole of this work of primary production

[1] London, Faber and Faber, 1951. See Chapter V, *The Reservoir of Talent*.

QUO VADIS?

could be carried out by between 5 and 10 per cent of mankind. What of the other 90 or 95 per cent? They are or will be occupied, more or less happily, in what used to be called taking in one another's washing. Thanks to the recent promulgation of Parkinson's Law this phenomenon is now explained in that we now know that work expands

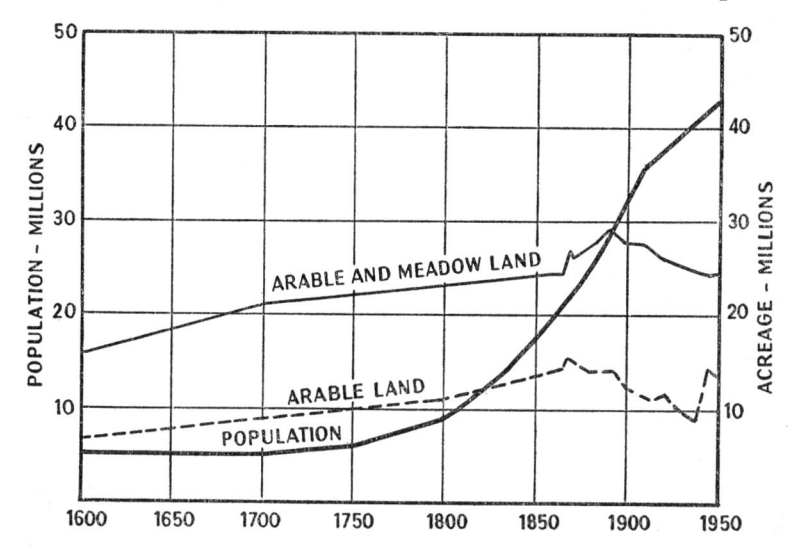

Fig. 42
Population and Improved Land in England and Wales

according to the time available for its execution. We can look forward to a world of ever-expanding towns set in a sparsely populated countryside inhabited by what have been called the primary and secondary rural population (the actual producers and their dependants, together with those essential to maintain services and social structure), together with a number, varying with the aesthetic attractiveness of the area concerned, of the adventitious population living in the country by choice.

A factor of major importance will be the ever-increasing mobility of the population. It is difficult to see any logical end to the demand for the individually owned automobile on the basis of one per family, two-car families balancing the non-owners. The position has already been reached in the United States of one private car per three persons. On a world basis at the present day this would give nearly 1,000,000,000 private cars, apart from the demands of commercial transport—another 200,000,000.

QUO VADIS?

There are other important aspects of increased mobility. Per head of population the demand for food, once it has reached one SNU of 1,000,000 Calories a year produced or 2,460 a day consumed, is relatively inelastic. But more and more time and money will be available for recreation. There seems nothing in the way of an almost limitless expansion of what is sometimes called tourism or the tourist industry—already recognized as probably the world's largest industry measured in numbers of persons engaged directly or indirectly and in money changing hands. In passing, it may be suggested that the development of the tourist industry may be a factor of enormous importance in our developing world. As an old Scottish Canadian friend of mine, who spent his winters lecturing in the States on the beauties of the Canadian Rockies and his summers showing them to visitors, was fond of saying: 'I like selling scenery because at the end you still have it.' Scenery, natural or man-made, glories of the past or achievements of the moment, are possessions a nation is proud to have and display: a source of income into which the dreaded charity need not enter.

The Ideal Climate

With this increased mobility, will there be a shift in the main populated areas? Will man now turn more to the tropics? If so, how is he adapted for life in the tropics?

By nature it would seem that man is a tropical animal. He lacks a protective natural fur against the cold, and it would seem his invasion and settlement of temperate and cold lands awaited and depended upon his discovery of fire and the development of clothing. In moving away from the tropics a use was made in very early times of caves for shelter and of huts within both of which man created his own artificial climate. This he has gone on doing, to a steadily increasing degree, ever since. The Australian aboriginal seems to afford the solitary example of a human being able to resist in the nude or near nude considerable degrees of cold; for all other human beings life is spent within buildings where a temperature for a large part of the year is maintained above, often far above, the natural temperature of the region. The extreme is reached in such regions as the heart of Canada, with winter temperatures far below freezing, where there may be a difference of 100 or 120 degrees Fahrenheit between the temperature maintained within buildings and that outside and where man normally passes the whole of his time for months on end in his artificial climate.

QUO VADIS?

Yet curiously little exact information exists as to the climatic conditions under which man functions, physically and mentally, at his optimum. This question of an ideal climate is now assuming an importance as never before. It is now just as easy, and a good deal cheaper, to cool a building in an over-hot climate as it is to heat a building in an over-cold climate. On this simple fact may rest a complete reorientation of world civilization. Though over-simplification is dangerous, it would seem that the early civilizations of Sumer, Akkad, Babylon, Egypt, India, Java and elsewhere, including the early civilizations of tropical Africa and Central America, flourished in the tropics where, some would claim, both individuals and nations reached maturity early. That many of them flourished in arid lands is obvious and it has been argued that the very need for men to band themselves together to produce an irrigation-civilization led to political and social organization—and so to progress—not required in the more humid tropics, where Nature provides man with food at little effort from the recipient.

The city-state of the Greeks and the urban civilization of the Romans can be collated at least in part with environmental conditions, but both evolved in sunny lands where the cold of winter is of short duration. The later development of France, Germany, Britain, North America, the Scandinavian countries and Russia into great powers with a virile civilization has been likened to the supposedly later maturing of the individual in colder climates. In each case a large proportion of life is led in an artificial climate, the character of which has happened rather than being the result of deliberate research and planning.

In the famous first edition of his *North America*, the late Professor J. Russell Smith, for so long the inspiration of successive generations of students at Columbia University, the opening sentence read: 'Hell is hot: have you ever wondered why?' The idea of hell was developed as part of the religious concepts of the eastern world where the extreme heat of summer was something far more to be dreaded than the pleasant cool of winter. To the Eskimo a hot hell was more likely to appeal as a desirable goal: an ultra-cold one was obviously something to be dreaded.

So the reaction of the European settlers on the North American continent against the cold of winter, so much more intense than in their homeland, was to intensify the artificial warmth of their homes. Three centuries later this has indeed become part of the American Way of Life. An indoor temperature of about 80° F., relatively dry, has become standard. The necessity of making any change in clothing be-

QUO VADIS?

tween summer and winter is avoided and man functions once again as a tropical animal, though avoiding the high humidity of the wet tropics. On those parts of the continent of Europe where winter temperatures are low the general standard of house warming is similar. In Britain the maritime climate with its mild winters—January average 38° to 44° F.— and cool summers—July average 55° to 63° F.—presents problems particularly because day temperatures of 50° F. or even 60° F. may commonly occur in winter, whilst in midsummer the thermometer may obstinately refuse to rise above 45° or 50° F. The British way of life still decrees a change into winter clothes—under, middle and top—and a summer reluctance to discard them, and a vast majority of homes devoid of other than the most casual heating in winter except in a favoured living-room and kitchen.

So the problem of the ideal climate remains and immense sums of money are being wasted because it has not been seriously studied. Looking back to the days of the British Raj in India it is staggering to contemplate the cost which was involved in building two complete capitals, Delhi and Simla, respectively for winter and summer use, paralleled by many dual capitals of the provinces such as Calcutta—Darjeeling, Madras and Ooty. At the same time buildings with thick walls, wide shady but useless verandas and double roofs were being built, within whose walls the hot air was to be gently agitated at first by battalions of punkah-wallahs pulling the cords of suspended punkahs, and then later by innumerable whirring electric fans.

The modern concept of air-conditioning enables many problems to be solved simultaneously. There is the problem of cold in winter and heat in summer, the problem of humidity control and protection from rain and damp, the danger of draughts, the problem of pure air, now so much more important when fog has become chemically charged smog, and when the destructive power of dirt, irritant dust and pollen, and germs can be curbed.

The problem in a very practical form was put to me a short time ago by a group of university vice-chancellors in India. We want, they said, to build a new university, completely air-conditioned, where the students will live and work for the nine months in the year of their university residence. One vice-chancellor claimed that since his library had been air-conditioned student use had more than trebled, and he believed actual study hours had increased by 30 per cent and the time had been more effectively used.

But what, in such circumstances, is the ideal climate? At present I

QUO VADIS?

know of no adequate answers; indeed some of the answers are contradictory, and there are many who, whilst accepting the heating of air, refuse to believe that the cooling of air can be beneficial.

It would seem that there are still some fundamental questions to be answered.

First, should the indoor temperature be related to outdoor? It would seem that human beings can safely enter a temperature of between 70° and 80° F. however cold the outside temperature and become adjusted to it in a matter of seconds. On the other hand, to come from an outdoor temperature of, say, 100° to 110° F. directly into an indoor temperature of 70° F. can be very dangerous. Cases of pneumonia can be attributed directly to the sudden shock. It is probable therefore either that there must be adjustment by an intermediate stage, or the indoor temperature must not differ from that outside by more than a certain number of degrees. It may be that some unspecified figure below blood-heat (98·4° F.) is a safe one.

In the second place, should the indoor temperature be constant, or should it have a diurnal variation together with, or without, a seasonal? If private preferences are a guide, many prefer a lower temperature in a bedroom.

In the third place, should provision, apart from the obvious need to replace stale air by fresh, be made for movement of air, or should it be still?

In the fourth place, what is the desirable relative or actual humidity —and again, should it be varied?

Fifth, if air is cleaned and filtered, are those living in it rendered more liable to air-borne germs or irritants when they enter the normal atmosphere?

Sixth, are conditions of temperature and humidity the same for sedentary brain workers as for manual workers?

Perhaps the only answers to these questions are by experiment in trial and error, but there are clearly cases where the construction of completely air-controlled buildings is long overdue. One is for hospitals—the stronghold of curious archaisms regarding 'fresh' (?) air, and the virtues of 'hardening' the patient to cold and uncontrolled draughts. The same strange concept of virtue is still associated with many of the schools and, so far as they still exist, with the stately homes of Scotland even more than of England.

QUO VADIS?

The Next Stage

It may seem strange to end this book by an inconclusive disquisition on the Ideal Climate. But the choice is deliberate because it seems in a way to highlight the present position. As a factor of the environment the weather conditions from hour to hour and day to day influence our every action, yet we have so little exact knowledge of the effect of weather and climate on our physical and mental well-being. We cannot even define scientifically what we mean by 'bracing' or 'enervating'. The same is true of nearly every aspect of human ecology: so little knowledge; so much waiting to be investigated. How can we plan for the future when there are so many unknown factors? Yet both the present and the future are a challenge to man's ability to adapt himself to a changing world. It is a developing world and I shall have achieved my object if I have persuaded my readers of the need to read, mark, learn and inwardly digest—and then to think anew.

INDEX

Acacia, 55
Acre-yields compared, 73–7
Africa, 20, 94, 104, 136, 169
Africa, South, 149
Africa, West, 148
African Regional Scientific Conference, 53
Agricultural Efficiency, measurement, 104
Agricultural Revolution, 80; in Britain, 160
Agriculture Act, 1947, 91
Agriculture, decreasing, 158
Agriculture, intensity of, 106
Agriculture and Internal Improvement, Board of, 93
Agriculture and Soils of Kent, Surrey and Sussex, 92
Air-conditioning, 186
Air photographs, 94, 154; in soil survey, 94
Air Surveys, 150, 154
Alkalinity, 61
Al Kharj oasis, 61
Aluminium, 139
Amazon basin, 50
America, Latin, 134
America, South, 136
American way of life, 169
Ammonium sulphate, 88
Anglo-Saxon settlers in Britain, 95, 151
Animal husbandry, 85
Antarctica, 13
Anthracite, world production, 128
Antimony, 149

Arabia, 136
Arid areas, 43, 53
Artificial insemination, 86
Asbestos, 149
Atomic power stations, in Britain, 125

Bacteria in soil, 91
Bahrain Island, 146
Baobab, 55
'Basin' cultivation, 100
Basin irrigation, 95, 101
'Basin lister', 100
Bathurst, 56
Bauxite, chief sources, 147
Bawdwin mines, 150
Belgian Congo, 148, 149
Bennett, H. H., 99
Bennett, J. W., 50
Bennett, M. K., 70
Berlin, Treaty of, 171
Birth control, 25
Birth rate: European, 24; Japanese, 24, 26; in United States, 24, 26
Bismuth, 149
'Blanket bog', 98
Bolivia, 148
Borgo a Mozzano, 88
Bowman, Isaiah, 146
Brazil, 15, 23; area, 37; mineral resources, 143
Britain, 15, 27, 28, 30, 85, 103, 125, 134, 151, 153; in war, 181
British Columbia, 148
British Commonwealth, area, 37
Burgdörfer, F. 33

INDEX

Burma, 136, 148, 150

Calder Hall, 125
Calories, 108
Caloric intake, 66, 70, 110, 111
Campos, 54
Canada, 123, 148, 167
Cane-sugar mills, 124
Car ownership, 183
Carr-Saunders, Sir Alexander, 19, 33
Carvajal, 50
Cassiterite, 148
Causes of death, England and Wales, 25
C.C.T.A., 53
Cereal production, 69; calories from, 69–70; consumption, 70
Ceylon, 50
Ceylon and its Capabilities, 50
Chalking, 95
Charcoal, 123
Chile, 148
China, 19, 21, 95, 120, 148; area, 37; erosion in, 99
Civilizations, effect of climate on, 185
Climate, ideal, 184–7
Climatic regions, 44–64
Climatic types, 44
Coal, 126, 127, 132
  in Africa, 134
  in Britain, 132
  distribution, 134
  in Europe, 134
  hydrogenation of, 132
  reserves, 124
  in U.S.S.R., 134
  world production, 131
  world production of bituminous, 129
Coalfields in Britain, 141
Coca-colonization, 169
Cocoa trees, 52
Cocoa, world production, 173
Colonial Geology and Mineral Resources, 150
Commission de Coopération Technique en Afrique au Sud du Sahara (C.C.T.A.), 53

Commodities, synthetic, 165–6
Conservation of land, 71
Copper, 148
Copper, chief sources, 147
Corn (maize), 75; yields in U.S.A., 75
Cover crops, 101
Crop productivity, 108
Crop yields, 105, 107
C.S.A., 53
Cultivable land, 39
Cyprus, land use, 155
Czechoslovakia, 128

Damodar Valley, 88
Darwin, Charles, 90
Death Control, 24
Death rate, 25
Debenham, Professor F., 60
Deep (quick) freezing, 85–6
Delft, 154
Demographic Yearbook (*Annuaire Démographique*), 17
Denmark, 158
Density of population, 120 *et seq.*
'Depressed Areas', 174
Developed Regions, 177
'Development Areas', 174
Diamonds, 149
Diet, need for varied, 70
Diet, types of, 112, 113
Dollar Curtain, 167
Dollar Empire, 168, 169

Earthworms, 96, 97
East African Ground-nut Scheme, 57
East Indies, 51, 136
Ecumene, 122
Egypt, 60, 79, 89
Electricity, transmission of, 126
Emigration policy, 27
Empires, 168
Energy in the Future, 127
Energy Resources of the World, 1949, 129
England and Wales, 121, 122
English-speaking population, 35
Epiphytes, 47

INDEX

Equatorial climate, 46–54 (see Tropical Rain-forest)
Essay on the Principle of Population as it affects the Future Improvement of Society, 14
Estate of Man, The, 182

Famine, 181
Fawcett, Professor C. B., 35, 39
Farmers of Forty Centuries, 120
Farming, chemicalization in Britain, 83
  efficiency in Britain, 87
  intensive, 91
  mechanization in Britain, 82
  specialized, 87
  subsistence, 158, 161
  type of, 103
Ferro-alloys, 149
Fertilizers, 84; chemical, 91
Finch and Trewartha, 46, 49
Fish culture, 89
Food, 65 *et seq.*
  in Britain, World War II, 68
  comparisons of production, 113
  composition of, 65
  consumption, animals, 112
  daily intake, 66
  estimates of world production, 68
  function of, 65
  monotonous, 66
  requirements, estimated, 111
  world production, 71
Food Composition Tables for International Use, 110
Forestry, 119
Forest, results of felling in Scotland, 98
Fragmentation of holdings, 88
France, 134, 158; area, 37
Fuel, 123, 124
Future Growth of World Population, The, 32, 33

Gas, natural, 126
Gaussen, Professor Henri, 155
Geneiri, 58
Geographical Situation of the United States in Relation to World Policies, 1948, 146
Geological erosion, control of, 100
Geological Survey, 92
Geophysical reconnaissance surveys, 150
Gerasimov, I. P., Academician, 63, 93
Germany, 148
Germany, East, 128
Germany, West, 128
Ghana, 100, 137, 154
Ghost towns, 141
Glinka, 93
Global land area, 13, 37
Gold, 141, 150
Gold production in Australia, 142
Gold Rush, 141, 145
Good husbandry, 91
Grassland, 118, 119
Great Soviet World Atlas, 63, 64, 93
Ground-nuts, 59
Gourou, Professor Pierre, 44
Guiana, British and Dutch, 148
Gully erosion, 99, 100
Gypsum (calcium sulphate), 94

Habitable globe, 38 *et seq.*
Hall, Sir A. Daniel, 92
Hammond, Sir John, 86
Hardpan, 56
Herbertson, A. J., 46, 48
Hevea braziliensis, 51
Hill pastures, improvement of, 120
Holdings, size of, 121
Hong Kong, 103; land use in, 155
Hoskins, H. L., 61
Housing density, 117
Humic Tropics, 53
Humus, 97
'Hungry season', 58, 60
Huntington, Ellsworth, 105, 106
Huxley, Sir Julian, 21
Hydro-electric power, 125
Hylea Research Institute, 53

India, 19, 70, 72, 78, 88, 89, 110, 120, 124, 160
India, caloric intake in, 112

INDEX

Indo-European races, 35
Indonesia, 148
Industrialization, 123; increasing, 158
Industrial Revolution, 80
I.N.E.A.C., 53
Infant mortality, 25
Inhabited areas, 39
International Geographical Union, 53, 153, 154
Iran, 136
Iraq, 136
Irrigation, 61
Irrigation and power development, 136
Israel, 125
Italy, 19

Jacks, G. V., 99
Jamaica, 148
Japan, 15, 19, 24, 72, 78, 89, 113, 119
Java, 51

Kariba Dam, 136; Gorge, 60
Katanga, the, 136, 148
Kellogg, C. E., 94
Kendall, Professor M. G., 105
Keyline Plan, 96
Killing diseases, 25
Kitimat power works, 148
Köppen, W., 46
Korea, 149
Kuczynski, R. R., 19
Kuwait, 123

Lake Victoria, 60
Land areas compared, 37
Land of Britain: Its Use and Misuse, The, 113, 121
'Land capability' classes, 94, 117, 118
Land, carrying capacity of, 112, 113, 114 (statistics)
Land classification, 113, 115 *et seq.*
Land Classification Map, 113
Land planning, 151
 quality of, 112
 resources, measurement of, 103
Land, stock-carrying capacity of, 119

Land for Tomorrow, 11
Land use, 42, 112, 151 *et seq.*
Land use, Gerasimov's analysis, 64
Land Utilisation Survey of Britain, 152
Leaching, 50
Less Developed Regions, 177, 179
Libya, 136
Lignite, 128
Linton, Professor David, 160
Llanos, 54
Loam, 95

Magnesium, 139
Malaya, 148
Malayan Peninsula, 51
Malnutrition, 58
Malthus, Thomas Robert, 14, 180
Manganese, 149
Man-made barriers, 181
Manual of Nutrition, 110
Marbut, C. F., 94
Marling, 95
Maternal mortality, 24
Meat, 119
Mediterranean climate, 44
Mestizos, 35
Mid-Latitudes, 61
 comparisons, 61
 crops, 62
 rainfall, 62
 temperatures, 61-2
 under-developed areas, 62
Millionaire Cities Today and Yesterday, 160
'Millionaire city', 160
Minerals, 124, 138-150, 179
 accessibility, 139
 in Africa, 145
 'economic', 138
 location, 139
 in the New World, 145
 production, effects of, 141
 reserves, 138
 in South America, 145
 in under-developed areas, 146 *et seq.*
 in U.S.S.R., 146

INDEX

Minerals Yearbook, 129
Mining, role of, 144 *et seq.*
Moisture deficiency, 85
Monlevade, 123
Monsoon conditions, 51
Mortality rates, 21
Mountainous areas, 43

National Incomes, 178
Nationalism, upsurge of, 176
'Negative areas', 38, 45
Negro population, 33
Netherlands, 120
Nevallon, 96
New Caledonia, 149
Nigeria, 148
Nile 60; alluvium, 95
Normans in Britain, 151
North America, 185
Northern Rhodesia, 148
Nuclear fission, 125

Ogg, Sir William, 83
Oil, 123, 126
    mineral, 132–3
    in N. Africa, 136
    occurrence of, 132
    producers, 134
    refineries, 126
    reserves of, 133
    shale, 133
    world production, 131
Oilfields, 124, 136
Orellana, 50
Osborn, Fairfield, 99
Our Plundered Planet, 99
Our Undeveloped World, 11, 31, 166
'Over-population', 103
Owen Falls, 60 136
Owen Falls Power Scheme 136

Paddy (rice) 76
Pakistan 78, 110, 120, 124, 160
Pakistan, Western, land reclamation in, 101
Parkinson's Law, 183
Patten Foundation Lectures, 11

Permafrost, 38, 41
Persian Gulf, 136
Peru, 101
Pests and diseases, control of, 84
Petroleum, estimated world resources and production, 130; sources, 135, *see also* Oil
Pinus sylvestris, 98
Plant geneticist, work of, 85
Point IV, 174
Population, age composition diagrams, 27–30
    changes, 1953–6, 16
    changing age structure, 26–7
    decreasing rural, 158
    density by political units, 22
    density, generalized distribution, 23
    distribution, 36
    mobility of, 183
    national contrasts, 31–2
    percentages engaged in agriculture, 159
    pressure, 13, 14 *et seq.*
    regional contrasts, 33, 34
    statistics, 114
    urban, 160
    world, 13, 17 *et seq.*, 180
    world rate of increase, 13, 19–20
Portugal, 149
Potential Production Unit, 117
Power, main sources, 126
Prassolov, L. I., 63
Protein intake, 69
Putnam, Palmer C., 127

Radium, 139, 149
Ranking coefficient, 108, 109
Rape of the Earth, The, 99
Recreation, 184
Resources, comparison of U.S.A., U.S.S.R., British Commonwealth, 164
Retirement, age of, 31
Rhodes, Cecil John, 169
Rhodes Scholarships, 169
Rice, 51, 52
Ripon Falls, 136

INDEX

'Robber' economy, 138
Roberts, Michael, 182
Rosov, N. N., 63
Rough grazing, 119
Royal Geographical Society, 63
Rubber, 165
Rural densities, 120 et seq.
  depopulation, 182
  population, adventitious, 121
  population, primary, 121
  population, secondary, 121
Russell, Sir John, 90, 92
Rye, 74

Sahara, 136
Saline incrustations, 94
Salt, 144
Sawmill waste, 123
School-leaving age, 31
Scientific Council for Africa south of the Sahara (C.S.A.), 53
Scotland, creation of bogs in, 98
Scots fir, 98
Scottish Soil Survey, 93
Scrub forest, 54
Settlement in Britain, 151
Shafi, M., 111
Shell Italiana, 88
Shifting cultivation, 101
Shokalskaia, Z. J., 94
Sindhri, 88
Skagway, 141
Smith, Professor J. Russell, 185
Soil conditioners, 85
  conservation, 99–100
Soil Conservation Service, 99
Soil erosion, 51, 96 et seq.
  erosion, man's part, 98
  erosion, natural protection against, 97
  formation, 97–8
  groups, Russian, 62–3
  'mining' of, 99
  population, 90
  profile, 92
  structure, 90 et seq.
Soil Survey Board in Britain, 92
  surveys, 92–4

surveys, comparison of national approach to, 93
surveys in United States, 93
surveys, value of, 94
texture, 94–6
Soils, development, 91
  immature, 98
'Special Areas', 174
Sphagnum, 98
Standard Nutrition Unit, 108, 111, 114
State of Food and Agriculture, The, 111, 176
Statistical Summary of the Mineral Industry, 150
Stockdale, Sir Frank, 146
Sugar cane, 77
Sukkar dam, 101
Swollen shoot disease, 52

Tariff walls, 170
Terracing, 101
Thailand, 148
Thornthwaite, C. W., 44
Tin, 140, 148; chief sources, 147
Tourist industry, 184
Town planning, 161; objective of, 15
Towns, drift to, 158; growth of, 182
Tropical cabinet woods, 47
Tropical Climate, 54 et seq. (see Tropical Savanna)
Tropical Monsoon Climate, 44
Tropical Rain-forest, 46–54
  crops, 51 et seq.
  development difficulties, 52
  pests and diseases, 52
  rainfall, 46–7
  soils, 47 et seq.
  temperatures, 46
  value of, 47
  vegetation, 47
Tropical Savanna, 54
  cattle in, 55
  grasslands, 55
  rainfall, 54, 56
  soils, 55
  temperatures, 54

INDEX

vegetation, 54
water supplies, 56
Tropics, development in, 57
  water control and irrigation in, 59–61
  water storage in, 60
Truman, President, 174
Tungsten, 149
Twinning in cattle, 86

Under-developed (undeveloped) areas, 174
Under-developed areas in mid-latitudes, 62
'Under-developed' countries, 124
Under-developed lands, 71, 136; fuel and power in, 133–7
Under-development, 123, 158; definition, 175
  in North America, 175
'Under-population', 103
UNESCO Arid Zone programme, 53
Uninhabitable areas, 124
U.S.S.R., area, 37, 93, 128
United Nations Organization, 17
United States, 15, 24, 113, 141, 148, 162–73, 183
  area, 37
  dilemma of, 165
  erosion in, 99
  help to under-developed countries, 165
  international investment, 171
  land resources, 162
  mineral resources, 163
  over-production in, 163, 166
  power consumption, 127
  self-sufficiency of, 165–6
  stockpiles, 167
  trade, 171
United States Commodity Credit Corporation, 166
Uranium, 139, 149
Urbanization, 158–61
Use of land, 15

Vanishing Lands, 99

Van Valkenburg, Professor Samuel, 105, 106, 153
Victoria Falls, 136
Village life, decline of, 88
Vince, S. W. E., 121
Vink, A. P. A., 118
Vitamins, 65
Volta Dam project, 137

Warping, 95
Waterlogging, 94
Water power, 136; resources, 137
Welfare State in Britain, 26
West Africa, farming methods in, 100
Western Pakistan, 94
Wheat yields, 67, 73
White population, 35
Whyte, R. O., 99
Wind power, 125
Wood as fuel, 123
World Land Use, 40–2
World Land Use Survey, 153; classification, 155–7
World Population, 19
World population, by continents, 20
  estimates, 18
  future growth, 21
World Population Survey, 157
World Population Trends, 1920–47, 17
World Power Conference, 1955, 124
World of the Soil, The, 90
World Soil Map, 63
World War I, 149
World War II, 27
Wyllie, James, 110

Yangambi, 53
Yangtse Delta, 120
Yellow races, 35
Yeomans, P. A. 96
Yukon, 141

Zambezi, R., 136
Zinc, world production, 142
Zuyder Zee, 13

HC 55
S75
1960

17515

Stamp, Lawrence Dudley
Our developing world

Date Due			
MR 25 '70			
MR 31 '71			

University of Pittsburgh at Bradford

DEMCO